ENTERTAINMENT ELECTRONICS

Anton Woodward

ENTERTAINMENT TECHNOLOGY PRESS

Systems Series

This book is dedicated to Auntie Bridget

ENTERTAINMENT ELECTRONICS

Anton Woodward

Entertainment Technology Press

Entertainment Electronics

© Anton Woodward

First published April 2015
Entertainment Technology Press Ltd
The Studio, High Green, Great Shelford, Cambridge CB22 5EG
Internet: www.etnow.com

ISBN 978 1 904031 81 9

A title within the
Entertainment Technology Press Systems Series
Series editor: John Offord

CODE / EE001_04-15

CONTENTS

PREFACE

Electronic engineering in theatres has become quite prevalent in recent years, whether for lighting, sound, automation or props – so it has become an increasingly important skill for the theatre technician to possess. This book is intended to give the theatre technician a good grasp of the fundamental principles of electronics without getting too bogged down with maths so that many of the mysteries of electronics are revealed.

Anton Woodward
February 2015

1 ELECTRON PHYSICS

All matter is made up from molecules, which in turn are made up from elements. There are just over 100 known elements. All elements are made up from various groupings of atoms from hydrogen (the lightest) to uranium (one of the heaviest). Atoms are extremely small, too small to be observed with a microscope, but atoms are in turn made up from sub-atomic particles – protons, neutrons and electrons. It is the last of these sub-atomic particles, the electron, that is at the heart of electronics.

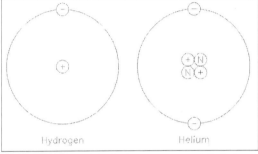

An atom can be thought of as a miniature solar system with a heavy nucleus made up of positively charged particles called protons and neutral particles called neutrons all surrounded by an orbit cloud of negatively charged electrons Overall the atom is

Atomic structure of the hydrogen atom and the helium atom.

electrically neutral, so the number of protons and electrons will always be the same in its stable state. These electrostatic forces hold the atom together. Different atoms will be made up from different compositions of these sub-atomic particles. For instance, hydrogen is made up from a single proton and a single electron with no neutrons, and is therefore the lightest atom. Helium has two protons, two neutrons and two electrons and is the next lightest atom.

In more complex atoms there will be more protons, neutrons and electrons. It is known that the nucleus of protons and neutrons, collectively known as nucleons, make up the vast majority of the mass of an atom with the cloud of orbiting electrons contributing very little to the mass but still balancing the electrical charge. The diameter of the nucleus is 1.75×10^{-15}m for hydrogen (the diameter of a single proton) to about

1.53×10^{-14}m for the heaviest atoms, such as uranium. These dimensions are much smaller than the diameter of the atom itself (nucleus + electronic cloud), by a factor of about 23,000 (uranium) to about 145,000 (hydrogen). The electrons in more complex atoms are known to be arranged in orbital shells and that each shell has a maximum number of electrons it can contain. The maximum number in the first shell is two, the maximum number in the second shell is eight and this maximum number continues in a progression as follows:

$2n^2$, where n is the shell number.

However, there are no known elements with more than 32 electrons orbiting in any one shell and there are only a maximum of seven known shells. This is a simplification and there are complex rules governing the number of electrons in sub-shells, however, for the purpose of electronics the above is enough information.

Chemical reactions and electronic migrations are all concerned with only the outer shell, the so-called valency shell, of any particular atom. If an outer shell is full, the atom is unable to react with any other atom and is therefore inert, such as helium.

However, if the outer shell is not full, the force binding them to the nucleus is relatively weak and the electrons are easily detached from one nucleus and attracted to an adjacent nucleus. Elements that contain freely moving electrons are called conductors and elements that do not contain (many) freely moving electrons are called insulators.

If an electrical potential is applied across the material the freely moving electrons will migrate more quickly toward the positive connection, and the motion of electrons is called an electric current. As electrons are being removed at the positive connection, they are being 'pumped' in at the negative connection. If the applied potential (Voltage) is increased the electrons will move faster, in other words the electrical current will increase. Whilst the electrons are moving they will collide with the atoms and other electrons and this will produce heat. Materials that allow this are called conductors and any particular material will obey Ohm's law, in that the relationship between the applied potential (V) and the current (I) that is produced will be a constant. This is called the materials resistance (R).

Resistance (R) = V/I

Where V is the applied potential in Volts and I is the current in Amps.

Not all electrical conduction is pure Ohmic; heating in particular can cause some materials to have complex *V*/*I* relationships.

If the outer shell electrons are tightly bound to the nucleus then a negligible number of electrons will be free to move. If an electrical potential is applied to such a material, very few electrons will move and the resultant current is small. These materials are called insulators.

Typical conductors are metals such as gold, silver, copper and aluminium, typical insulators are glass, porcelain, plastic, rubber and silicon. The last material, silicon, can be modified to behave as either a conductor or an insulator and can therefore become a semiconductor; this will be explained more fully later on.

Thermionic valve

If an electric potential is applied between two metal plates in a vacuum, then the electrons will leave the negative plate (cathode) and be attracted toward the positive plate (anode). Because there are no other particles in the vacuum, the migrating electron will travel in a straight line with no collisions. Current can only flow from the negative terminal (cathode) toward the positive terminal (anode); this one way motion of electrons is like a check valve for electrons and is called a diode.

This effect was used for many years and is called a vacuum valve diode. This unidirectional behavior is called rectification, and is used to convert alternating current to direct current, and to extract modulation from radio signals in radio receivers. By adding a heater next to the cathode, the electrons are more easily dislodged; these heated vacuum glass tube devices are called thermionic valves.

If an extra plate (grid) is inserted between the cathode and anode, and the potential is varied on this

Thermionic valve.

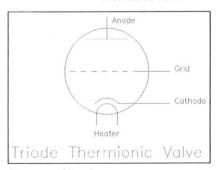

Diagram of Triode.

plate, then the overall electron current flow can be adjusted. This effect was first used to amplify small signals at the grid to produce large changes in current flow between the cathode and anode. This device is called a triode. There were further advances on this with more plates in the early twentieth century to produce tetrodes and pentodes. This manipulation of electron flow and the study of it is electronics!

Electrons and magnetic fields

The movement of electrons is called an electric current. However, the movement of electrons can be influenced by magnetic fields and similarly an electric current can produce a magnetic field. Electrons moving in an electric field will move in the direction of the applied potential, i.e. toward the attracting positive connection, but electrons moving perpendicular to a magnetic field will be subject to a force that is at right angles to the electrons movement. Electrons moving in the same direction as a magnetic field will be unaffected. Conversely, an electric current will produce a magnetic force that is at right-angles to the electric current. These are known as Flemings left and right hand rules. The left-hand rule is the 'motor' rule and the right hand rule is called the 'generator' rule.

The thumb represents thrust, the first finger represents field and second finger represents (conventional) current.

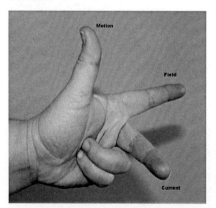
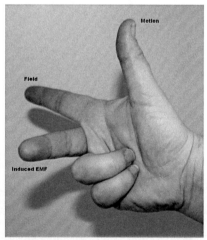

Flemming's left-hand and right hand rule.

Electron current and conventional current

Electricity was discovered around 1781, but the electron was not discovered until 1897. Between these two dates, scientists had to make an arbitrary decision as to which way they were going to decide as the direction for current flow; unfortunately they chose the wrong one! Ever since then, electronics engineers have had to work around a silly bit of history, designing their circuits with current flowing from positive to negative, while knowing that the particles themselves actually flow from negative to positive. This regularly causes confusion, but in reality does not often matter all that much as all the mathematics i.e. Ohm's law etc works out just the same.

2 SEMICONDUCTOR MATERIAL

Matter can exist in one of three states, solid, liquid and gas. The molecules in liquid and gas move freely but in solids do not move freely. Any movement in a solid is usually just the molecule vibrating around its designated position and this is observed as heat.

Some solids arrange themselves molecularly as crystals, such as salt, which means that no matter how large they get they will exhibit the same geometric molecular pattern.

At the atomic level, most substances are arranged in a similar crystal-like manner, in that they have very well defined atomic structures.

The majority of electrical conductors rely on its ability to produce and freely move electrons. The elements silicon and germanium both have four electrons in their outer orbit that results in a diamond shaped crystal – like atomic structure that does not readily move electrons and are therefore quite good insulators.

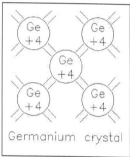

Germanium crystal.

However, by introducing a small impurity their conductivity can be dramatically altered. By introducing an atom of arsenic, that has five electrons in its outer shell but will fit snugly in the crystal-like structure, there will be an electron that is free from bonding and will be very mobile if an electric potential is applied. This is called 'doping'.

The quantity of free electrons can be determined easily by controlling the amount of doping. Conductance in the new substance is caused by an excess of negatively charged free electrons and is therefore called an n-type semiconductor.

If an atom with only three electrons in its outer shell is introduced, such as boron or indium, a similar effect occurs, in that there will be a

Germanium doped with arsenic.

deficiency of electrons and there will be 'holes' in the atomic structure. If an electric current is applied across the substance, the electrons will move toward the positive connection, but it gives the appearance of the holes moving toward the negative connection. This substance is called a p-type semiconductor because the impurity has created a positively charged substance.

There will still be some movement of electrons due to thermal effects, but these will be very much in the minority compared to what will be achieved by the effect of doping.

Germanium doped with boron.

If an n-type substance and a p-type substance are brought together to create a p-n junction, some of the excess electrons in the n-type material will cross into the p-type material and fill the holes and produce a depletion layer. There will be a small amount of charge across the actual layer, but there will be no voltage across the combined substance as a whole.

p-n junction and depletion layer.

If a voltage is applied to the p-n junction, with a positive connection at the p-type end of the substance and the negative connection at the n-type end of the substance, electrons will flow from the n-type material to the p-type material and holes will travel in the other direction, therefore current is flowing and the combined device is conducting.

If a voltage is applied to the p-n junction, with a negative connection at the p-type end of the substance and the positive connection at the n-type end of the substance, electrons will flow from the n-type material to the negative connection and holes will travel in the other direction for a very short time and then current will not flow, the depletion layer is increased and the combined device will not conduct (except for minor effects of heat).

There is therefore a small, but important, asymmetrical voltage vs current relationship. A small forward bias is required to get the p-n junction conducting; this relates to the charge on the depletion layer and is about 0.2 Volts for germanium and 0.7 Volts for silicon.

On its own the p-n junction makes an excellent rectifier just like the thermionic valve diode described earlier, and a single p-n junction is just that, a semiconductor diode. But the p-n junction can be put together in more complex ways to create other interesting electronic devices.

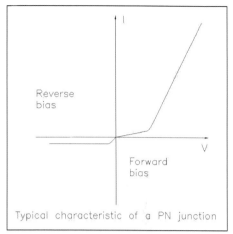

Characteristic of p-n junction.

3 UNITS

The various units used for describing and quantifying electron movement have names and symbols. The names are always printed in Roman letters but the symbols are always written in italic letters. Many of the unit names are named after people and it is therefore normal to use an initial capital letter as used for proper nouns when using them.

Electrical current (I) is measured in Amperes (Amp, A)	André-Marie Ampère
Electrical charge (Q) is measured in Coulombs (C)	Charles-Augustin de Coulomb
Potential (V) is measured in Volts (V) (also E, e.m.f, p.d.)	Alessandro Volta
Resistance (R) is measured in Ohms (Ω)	Georg Simon Ohm
Power (p) is measured in Watts (W)	James Watt
Conductance (G) is measured in Siemens (S)	Werner von Siemens
Resistivity (ρ) is measured in Ohm metre (Ωm)	See Ohm
Capacitance (C) is measured in Farads (F)	Michael Faraday
Magnetic field (B) is measured in Tesla (T)	Nikola Tesla
Inductance (L) is measured in Henry's (H)	Joseph Henry
Magnetic flux (φ) is measured in Weber (Wb)	Willhelm Weber
Frequency (f) is measured in Hertz (Hz)	Heinrich Hertz
Force (F) is measured in Newtons (N)	Isaac Newton

Current and Charge

The units above are interrelated to each other, time, other units and constants as the electrons move around an electronic circuit. If we start with the measurement of current, measured in Amps this is a fundamental measurement of force (F) in Newtons (N) (Isaac Newton) between two conductors (or coils) of given dimensions placed at a given distance apart in metres. The measurement of charge, the Coulomb is the amount of charge that passes a particular point in a circuit and one Coulomb is when a current of 1 Ampere flows for 1 second.

Therefore
$$\text{Charge} = \text{Current x time} \quad Q = It \quad \text{or} \quad I = \frac{Q}{t}$$

In other words Current (I) is the amount of Charge (Q) flowing through a circuit in a given time (t).

Voltage

The Voltage or potential at any point in an electronic circuit, or anywhere else for that matter, is defined as the energy (in Joules) (James Joule) in producing a charge of 1 Coulomb. It is therefore in effect the amount of energy required to move 1 Coulomb of charge to a particular place (in a static electrical field). On a practical level it is the Voltage potential between one point in an electrical circuit and another point in an electrical circuit. Often one of those points will be referred to as Ground potential, zero potential (0 Volts or 0V) or Earth. Sometimes, it is the negative terminal of a battery or power supply and is often 'strapped' to Earth such that there is no potential between that point in the electronic circuit and Earth. All other points in the electronic circuit will then be measured with respect to 0 Volts. Therefore any other point in the electronic circuit that is measured with a positive potential with respect to 0V means that work has to be done in order to move a positive charge toward it and conversely any other point in the electronic circuit that is measured with a negative potential with respect to 0V means that work has to be done in order to move a negative charge toward it. This is perhaps the most fundamental point; electronics is the study of the movement of electrons.

potential = energy/charge

$$V = \frac{I}{Q}$$

The electromotive force (E) (e.m.f) is the potential difference (p.d.) between two points in an electronic circuit when no current is flowing. When current is flowing there will be a Voltage drop across the battery or generator providing the e.m.f, therefore the p.d. is always less than the driving e.m.f.

Resistance

When current (*I*) flows through a conductor, the resistance (*R*) of that conductor causes the electrical energy to be converted into thermal energy. This will result in a drop of the potential along that conductor, creating a potential difference (p.d.) i.e. a Voltage (*V*) between the ends of the conductor. The resistance (*R*) of the conductor is therefore defined by:

$$Resistance = p.d./current \qquad R = \frac{V}{I}$$

This is universally known as Ohm's Law and is the most important equation for understanding the movement of electrons. Other forms of the equation are:

$$V = IR \quad \text{and} \quad I = \frac{V}{R}$$

Power

Power (p) is the rate at which work is done and is measured in Watts (W). When electrical energy is converted to thermal energy, such as when a current flows through a conductor as described above, then the power dissipated is given as:

$$P = IV = I \times IR = I^2R$$

$$P = IV = V/R \times V = V^2/R$$

Conductance

Conductance (G) is the inverse of Resistance (R). Nowadays it is measured in Siemens (S); an older name is mho (literally Ohm spelt backwards!).

$$G = \frac{1}{R}$$

Resistivity

Different materials will exhibit different levels of resistance and this is known as their resistivity. It is a measure of how strongly a material opposes the flow of electric current. A low resistivity indicates a material that readily allows the movement of electric charge. The SI unit of electrical resistivity is the Ohm metre (Ωm). It is commonly represented by the Greek letter ρ (rho).

$$\text{Resistance of material } (R) = \frac{\rho L}{A}$$

Where A is the cross-sectional area in meters and L is its length in metres.

Capacitance

As Charge (Q) flows into a capacitor, a p.d. will build up across that device. The capacitance (C) is measured in Farads (F) and is given by:

$$\text{Capacitance} = \text{charge/p.d.} \qquad C = \frac{Q}{V}$$

Magnetic Field

The magnetic field (B) created by a current flowing through a conductor is measured in Tesla (T). If a conductor of length (L) is carrying a current (I) and the angle between the magnetic field and the conductor is Θ, then the force (F) in Newtons (N) on the conductor is given by:

$$F = BI.L \sin \Theta$$

The force at right angles, i.e. 90°, Sin90° = 1, so

$$F = BI.L$$

For a circular coil of N turns and radius r, the magnetic field (or magnetic flux density) at the centre of the coil is:

$$B = \mu_o NI/2r$$

Where μ_o is the constant of permeability of free space and has a value of $4\pi \times 10^{-7} = 1.2566 \times 10^{-6}$

At a distance d from the centre of the coil (along its axis) the magnetic field will be:

$$B = \mu_o NI/2 \times r^2/(r^2 + d^2)^{3/2}$$

If the magnetic field is 1T, the magnetic flux is 1 Weber (Wb) per square metre. A magnetic flux of 1Wb in a coil of 1 turn will produce an e.m.f of 1 Volt if the flux is reduced to zero in 1 second.

The two points made above are important for motors and generators.

Inductance

The inductance (L) of a coil is measured in Henry's (H). If a coil of 1H is passing a current of 1A then a magnetic flux of 1Wb will be produced.

$$L = N \varphi/I$$

The self-inductance (M) of a coil is equivalent to the e.m.f induced into that coil when the current changes at a rate of 1A per second.

$$E = -L.dI/dt$$

The mutual inductance of two coils is 1H if a current of 1A in the primary coil induces a magnetic flux of 1Wb in the secondary coil.

Frequency

The frequency (f) in an electronic circuit is the number of times an event happens in 1 second and is measured in Hertz (Hz). The event may be electrical pulses, or the repetition of a waveform such as a sinewave, square-wave or triangle wave.

Force

The Newton (**N**) is the SI derived unit of force, named after Sir Isaac Newton in recognition of his work on classical mechanics. It is equal to the amount of net force required to accelerate a mass of one kilogram at rate of one metre per second squared.

Force = mass x acceleration $\quad F = ma$

This is known as 'Newton's second law of motion'.

Multiples and sub-multiples of units

Many of the units given are often expressed in multiples or sub-multiples, just as weight is measured kilograms or power as MegaWatts, volume as millilitres or distance as micrometers. So, too, are the SI units used in electronics subject to prefixes.

The prefixes for multiple units are as follows:				
Base		Prefix	Symbol	Example
10^3	(Thousand)	kilo	k	kV, kiloVolt
10^6	(Million)	Mega	M	MΩ, MegaOhm
10^9	(Thousand Million)	Giga	G	GV, GigaVolt
10^{12}	(Million Million)	Tera	T	TΩ, TeraOhm
The prefixes for sub-multiples are as follows:				
10^{-3}	(Thousandth)	milli	m	mV, milliVolt
10^{-6}	(Millionth)	micro	μ	μF, microFarad
10^{-9}	(Thousand Millionth)	nano	n	nA, nanoAmp
10^{-12}	(Million Millionth)	pico	p	pF, picoFarad

4 RESISTORS

The resistor is the most widely used electronic component.

A resistor determines the flow of current in a circuit. The higher the value of the resistor in Ohms, the more it resists current flow, so resistance is inversely proportional to current flow. Resistance (**R**), current (**I**) and Voltage (**V**) are connected by Ohm's Law.

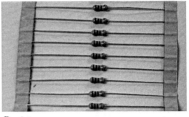

Resistors.

$$R = V/I \qquad \text{or} \qquad I = V/R \qquad \text{or} \qquad V = R \times I$$

Resistors are available in a wide range of values from fractions of an Ohm to millions of Ohms (MΩ). They are available in a wide range of power ratings from fractions of a Watt to millions of Watts (MW). As a resistor passes current, energy is absorbed in the form of heat, and the temperature rises until the heat radiated equals the heat absorbed. This temperature rise determines the maximum wattage a resistor can dissipate and is equal to I^2R Watts.

The simplest and most widely used resistor is the carbon type and is manufactured from a small rod of carbon, moulded to provide the required value of resistance, with leads brought out at each end. They are then encapsulated to protect them and given a colour code to identify their resistance and tolerance. Carbon type resistors are available from 1/8W to 2W and have values from a few Ohms to around 10MΩ. The effect of heating in carbon resistors will change the resistance to some extent and are therefore not suitable for applications where great precision is required, in which case an alternative would be the thin-film type resistor. Applications that require higher powers to be dissipated use wire-wound resistors.

The resistor colour code consists of up to five bands, the first two bands will give a number, the third band is the multiplier band and the fourth band will give the tolerance.

Colour	1st band 1st Digit	2nd Band 2nd Digit	3rd band Multiplier	4th Band Tolerance
Black	—	0	1	—
Brown	1	1	10	+/− 1%
Red	2	2	100	+/− 2%
Orange	3	3	1000	
Yellow	4	4	10,000	—
Green	5	5	100,000	—
Blue	6	6	1,000,000	—
Violet	7	7	10,000,000	—
Grey	8	8	100,000,000	—
White	9	9	1,000,000,000	
Silver	—	—	0.01	+/− 10%
Gold	—	—	0.1	+/− 5%
None	—	—	—	+/− 20%

Occasionally there is a 5th band that denotes temperature co-efficient (tempco) and is given in parts per million change of resistance per degree Kelvin (or Celsius).

Fixed resistors are normally manufactured in a series called the E12 series; this has 12 values in each decade. The standard values are:

10   12   15   18   22   27   33   39   47   56   68   82

The series repeats in higher and lower decades, so for instance, taking 47 as a standard value, resistors are available as:

4.7Ω, 47Ω, 470Ω, 0.47kΩ, 4.7kΩ, 47kΩ, 470kΩ, 0.47MΩ, 4.7MΩ, 47MΩ, 470MΩ

As an example, using the above colour code and a standard resistor of 47Ω, with a 5% tolerance, i.e. the resistor is guaranteed to have a value somewhere between 44.65Ω and 49.35Ω then the colour code will be:

1st Band	2nd Band	3rd Band	4th Band
Yellow	Violet	Black	Gold

A 47Ω resistor.

More examples:

1st Band	2nd Band	3rd Band	4th Band	
Red	Red	Red	Gold	22 x 100 = 2.2kΩ ±5%
Green	Blue	Yellow	Silver	56 x 10,000 = 560kΩ ±10%
Blue	Grey	Gold	Brown	68 x 0.1 = 6.8Ω ±1%

There are also the E24, E48 and E96 series but they are not used very often. However, they can be useful where, for an instance, a resistance of 11kΩ is required and 10kΩ or 12kΩ, is not near enough and using 10kΩ and 1kΩ resistors in series is not practical.

Resistors are also available as surface mounted devices (SMD) and in this case their value is given by a three digit number, where the first two digits provide the value in Ohms and the third digit provides the number of zero's following the number. For example the number 472 would be 4700Ω or 4.7kΩ.

Resistors in series

When two or more resistors are connected in series their total resistance is the sum of their individual resistances.

$$R_T = R_1 + R_2 + R_3 + ... + R_n$$

If resistors of the same value and tolerance are connected in series, then the total working Voltage is the sum of the individual working Voltages and the tolerance, power rating and tempco is unchanged.

By adding two resistors from the E12 series it is possible to produce all the values from the E24 series.

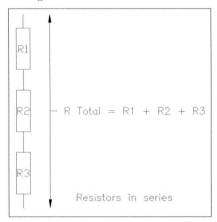

Three resistors in series.

Resistors in parallel

When two or more resistors are connected in parallel their total resistance is given by:

$$\frac{1}{RT} = \frac{1}{R1} + \frac{1}{R2} + \frac{1}{R3} + \ldots + \frac{1}{Rn}$$

If only two resistors of the same value are connected in parallel, then their combined resistance is halved, but very usefully, their combined power rating is doubled.

Three resistors in parallel.

This is a useful way of dealing with high power requirements, if a higher wattage resistor is not available. The tolerance remains unaffected.

Variable resistors

Resistors are also available as variable resistors as rheostats or slide resistors. They operate on the principle of the potential divider and are often called potentiometers. They are usually either a rotary device or a slide device, although there are some all electronic devices that accomplish the same task.

Variable resistors are available as linear, logarithmic or anti-logarithmic devices. The

Various potentiometers.

linear variable resistor has a simple linear relationship between the slider position and the resistance value. The logarithmic and anti-logarithmic variable resistors follow a log curve and are primarily used for audio volume and balance controls to compensate for the human ear response.

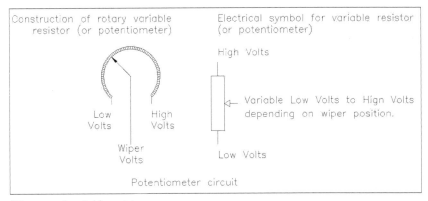

Diagram of variable resistor.

5 VARISTORS

A varistor is a resistor that varies its resistance with Voltage. They are sometimes referred to as Voltage Dependant Resistors (VDR). The resistance is high at low Voltage and decreases with increasing Voltage. They are primarily used to protect electronic circuits that are sensitive to excessive Voltages. This is done by shunting the load with the varistor such that when the Voltage is excessive the current will flow through the varistor instead. This is designed to cope with very short duration Voltage spikes (< 20μS) such as that encountered during a thunder storm. They are not designed to be used for a long duration. If they are used for a long duration they may melt or explode which may

A typical varistor.

be a fire hazard, they therefore usually have a fuse in series with them. The most common type is the Metal Oxide Varistor (MOV) and is made from zinc oxide. A varistor will have a Voltage rating below which it can be considered 'open-circuit' and above which it can be considered 'short-circuit'. A varistor's performance will degrade with repeated Voltage spikes, however as its energy rating increases its life expectancy increases exponentially.

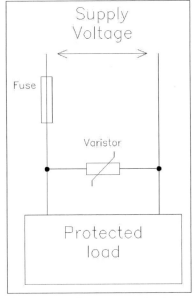

A varistor used to protect a circuit.

6 CAPACITORS

Capacitors are electrical energy accumulators, which mean that they can store a charge for a period of time. This makes them very useful devices for smoothing Voltages, de-coupling, filters and tuned circuits. They are manufactured in a wide range of values and working Voltages to suit different applications.

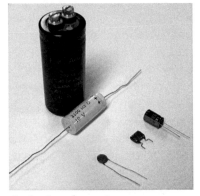

A capacitor is composed of two metal plates with an isolation layer between them. When a Voltage is applied across a capacitor a charging

A selection of capacitors.

flow of electrons takes place. The amount of electron flow depends on the Voltage applied, the size of the plates, and the size of the gap between the plates and what material has been used for the isolation layer, otherwise known as the dielectric layer.

The construction of a capacitor is given by the following formula:

$$C = \frac{\varepsilon A}{d}$$

Where C is Capacitance in Farads, ε is the permittivity of material between the plates, A is the area of the plates and d is the separation of the plates. To increase capacitance it is therefore necessary to increase plate area (A) or permittivity (ε) or decrease the plate separation (d).

A simple plate capacitor is shown in figure (a), however a capacitor constructed like this would be unlikely to provide enough capacitance for most purposes, so construction in practical capacitors is more like figure (b).

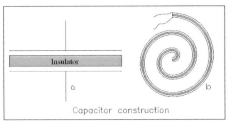

Capacitor construction (a) parallel plate, (b) ceramic capacitor.

Figure b shows an interleaved

type construction with foil and high permittivity dielectric material like mica or ceramics; this type of construction can produce capacitors with values from a few pF to around 5000pF.

Larger capacitor values can be constructed using foil and paper, or polyester or polycarbonate in alternate layers. Even greater capacitance values can be attained by immersing a plate in an electrolyte, a very thin layer (typically 10^{-4}mm) of oxide film forms which behaves as the dielectric. However, an electrolytic capacitor's dielectric oxide layer will break down and subsequently explode if a reverse polarity Voltage is applied across it, so it is important that the correct polarity is always used. In general electrolytic capacitors are to be avoided where possible because they have quite high leakage and tend to dry out and consequently have short lives. However, having said that the only way to get the high capacitances required for power supplies (especially at higher Voltages) is by using the electrolytic capacitor.

The list of capacitor types below indicates the general properties of different types of capacitors that are available.

Type	Capacitance	Working Voltage
Mica	2.2pF – 10nF	250V – 650V d.c.
Ceramic	1nF - 1µF	250V – 650V d.c.
Polypropylene	1nF - 1µF	1000V d.c. or more
Polycarbonate	2.2pF – 10nF	Less than 250V d.c.
Polyester	1nF - 1µF	250V – 650V d.c.
Polystyrene	2.2pF – 10nF	1000V d.c. or more
Electrolytic	1µF and more	1000V d.c. or more
Tantalum	1µF and more	Less than 250V d.c.

Capacitor value code

The value of a capacitor can be given in one of several ways; it may simply be printed, especially on larger electrolytic capacitors or it may be given as a three digit number or as a colour code. If given as a three digit number then the first two digits is the capacitance in picoFarads (pF) and the third digit is the number of zero's following the two digits (multiplier). For example 473 would be 47000pF (47nF). If there is a letter it indicates tolerance where J is ±5%, K is ±10%, M is ±20% and Z is -20%/+80%.

The colour code for ceramic capacitors is as follows:

	1st Band	2nd Band	3rd Band
Black	-	0	x1
Brown	1	1	x10
Red	2	2	x100
Orange	3	3	x1000
Yellow	4	4	x10000
Green	5	5	-
Blue	6	6	-
Violet	7	7	-
Grey	8	8	x0.01
White	9	9	x0.1

Capacitance is in picoFarads (pF)

For example a capacitor with red, red, red banding would be 2200pF (2.2nF).

For tantalum capacitors it is very similar except the basic capacity is in microfarads (μF) not picoFarads (pF).

Just like resistors, capacitors are generally manufactured in an E12 type scale consisting of 12 values that are repeated in higher and lower decades.

10   12   15   18   22   27   33   39   47   56   68   82

So, for example,
2.2pF, 22pF, 220pF, 2.2nF, 22nF, 220nF, 2.2μF, 22μF, 220μF, 2200μF would be typical values for capacitors, starting with perhaps mica type capacitors and ending with electrolytic type capacitors. Electrolytic capacitors have such low tolerances that they are only usually available in a few of the range, typically 10, 22 and 47 in each decade.

Capacitors in series

When two or more capacitors are connected in series the total capacitance is given by the formula:

$$\frac{1}{CT} = \frac{1}{C1} + \frac{1}{C2} + \frac{1}{C3} + \ldots + \frac{1}{Cn}$$

Therefore if two identical capacitors are connected in series their total capacitance is halved (the way to think of it is that the dielectric gap has doubled).

$$1/C \text{ Total} = 1/C_1 + 1/C_2 + 1/C_3$$

Capacitors in series

Capacitors in series.

Capacitors in parallel

When capacitors are connected in parallel the total capacitance is given by the formula:

$$C_T = C_1 + C_2 + C_3 + \ldots + C_n$$

Therefore if two identical capacitors are connected in parallel their total capacitance is doubled (the way to think of it is that the area of the plates has doubled).

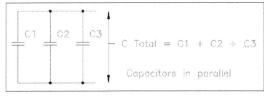

$$C \text{ Total} = C_1 + C_2 + C_3$$

Capacitors in parallel

Capacitors in parallel.

All capacitors will have a maximum working Voltage that should not be exceeded. When designing a circuit the maximum peak Voltage (not RMS) including transients must be determined and care should be taken to select capacitors accordingly.

Variable capacitors

Capacitors are also manufactured as variable devices. They are particularly useful in LC tuned circuits for oscillators and radios. In order for a capacitor to be variable one of the main construction parameters has to be varied: plate area (A), permittivity (ε) or plate separation (d). Most variable capacitors use air as the dielectric layer and two sets of metallic vanes that can be adjusted to effectively alter the amount of plate area that is facing each other. Other methods include altering the distance between the plates in smaller trimmer type variable capacitors. Varying the dielectric is not generally used, although some instrumentation transducers use this method. The Varicap (described more fully in the diode chapter) is also a variable capacitor that achieves its variability by effectively altering the distance between the plates by altering the thickness of the depletion layer in the p-n junction.

A variable capacitor.

7 INDUCTORS

An inductor (or reactor) is a passive electronic component that can store energy in a magnetic field created by the electric current passing through it. An inductor's ability to store magnetic energy is measured by its inductance (L), in units of Henry's (H). Inductors are coils of wire wound around a former; indeed they are often called coils. As an electronic device they are used for several purposes including as a choke, a tuning coil, a transformer or as an energy-storage inductor.

A choke inductor.

A choke functions like a resistor in an alternating current (AC) circuit by opposing changes in current through it by developing a Voltage across it that is proportional to the rate of change of the current. Therefore the inductive reactance (X_L) of the circuit is dependent on both the inductance (L) of the coil and the frequency (f) of the alternating current (AC).

$$X_L = 2\pi f L$$

When combined with a capacitor they can form a tuned circuit which can be used for tuning, or passing certain frequencies or blocking certain frequencies. If more than one coil are wound on a single former they can be used as a transformer (refer to chapter on transformers). As an energy storage inductor they are used for smoothing in power supplies.

An 'ideal inductor' has inductance, but has no resistance or capacitance, and does not dissipate or radiate energy. However, in the real world, inductors will have some resistance due to the resistance of the wire and some capacitance due to the adjacent turns of wire. At low frequencies these have little effect but at greater frequencies the resistance of the coil will become greater due to 'skin effect' and the capacitance will have greater effect to the point where the overall impedance (refer to chapter on AC theory for explanation of Impedance) of the coil becomes capacitive rather than inductive.

Inductors are constructed by winding a coil of wire around a former that might have air or a ferromagnetic material inside it. Ferromagnetic materials have higher permeability than air and so will allow for inductors of greater inductance to be formed. Low frequency inductors are usually formed on layers of steel laminates to reduce eddy currents in order to reduce losses due to heating. It is also possible to form an inductor by printing a spiral on a printed circuit board.

Air Core Inductor

An air core inductor is a coil that is wound on a plastic or ceramic former that does not have any ferromagnetic material in it – it has just air. This will create an inductor with a lower inductance than if it had had ferromagnetic material in it. However, they are often used at high frequencies and so do not suffer from core losses that a ferromagnetic core inductor would. An interesting effect of air coils that are free to move on their formers is that they will display a phenomenon known as microphony; that is, that their inductance will change with mechanical vibration (refer to Chapter 15).

Ferromagnetic Core Inductor

A ferromagnetic core inductor is a coil that is wound on a magnetic core such as ferromagnetic material. This will increase the inductance by a factor of several thousand over an air core inductor but at the cost of energy losses known as core losses. These losses are caused by two main factors, the first being due to eddy currents, that is where a current is induced into the core material itself and is then lost as heat. The other is known as hysteresis loss; that is where the alternating current that is induced into the coil is lost as the magnetic domains shift. Both of these losses increase linearly with the frequency of the alternating current. If the current is too high then the magnetic core will saturate and the inductance will change with current flow and will therefore become non-linear. Therefore in circuits that require linearity, such as audio circuits, it is important not to saturate the magnetic core by having too much current flowing through it.

Ferrite Core Inductor

A ferrite core inductor is similar to a ferromagnetic core inductor except that the ferrite is a ceramic ferromagnetic material that does not conduct and will not therefore allow eddy currents to flow. The ferrite also has low coercivity (low magnetism) to keep hysteresis losses to a minimum. Ferrite core inductors are used at high frequencies, particularly in radio circuits.

Laminated Core Inductor

A laminated core inductor is a coil that is wound on stacks of thin steel sheets, otherwise known as laminations and are insulated. The insulation between the sheets prevents eddy currents and the sheets themselves are made of low coercivity silicon steel to keep hysteresis losses to a minimum. Laminated core inductors are used at low frequency, primarily as chokes. Transformers often use a laminated core construction for all the same reasons.

Variable Inductor

An inductor can be made to be variable by moving the ferromagnetic or ferrite core inside the coil. By adjusting the core material further into the coil, the magnetic permeability will increase thus increasing its inductance. This is particularly useful for tuning radio circuits.

Inductors in series

When two or more inductors are connected in series the total inductance is given by the formula:

$$L_T = L_1 + L_2 + L_3 + \ldots + L_n$$

Therefore if two identical inductors are connected in series their total inductance is doubled.

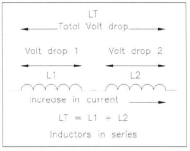

Inductors in series.

Inductors in parallel

When inductors are connected in parallel the total inductance is given by the formula:

$$\frac{1}{LT} = \frac{1}{L1} + \frac{1}{L2} + \frac{1}{L3} + \ldots + \frac{1}{Ln}$$

Therefore if two identical inductors are connected in parallel their total inductance is halved.

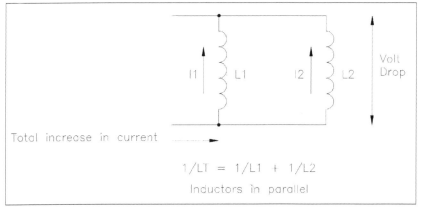

Inductors in parallel.

Stored energy

The energy (E), in Joules (J), stored in an inductor is equal to the amount of work required to establish the current through the inductor, and thus the magnetic field. This is given by the formula:

Energy Stored (E) = $\frac{1}{2}.LI^2$

Where L is inductance and I is the current flowing through the inductor.

Q Factor

A further important characteristic of an inductor is its quality (Q) factor. This is a measure of its selectivity or 'sharpness' at a particular frequency. Inductors with a high Q value are better inductors. Typical values range from about 20 to 100. Q is greater at higher frequencies and with inductors of higher inductance.

Q is the relationship between the reactive inductance and its resistance. As already stated a perfect inductor would not have any resistance and therefore its Q factor would be infinite. However, in the real world there will be some resistance because the coils are made from metal wire. The Q factor is the ratio of its inductive reactance to its electrical resistance at a given frequency, and is therefore a measure of its efficiency. The higher the Q factor of an inductor, the closer it behaves to an ideal lossless inductor.

The Q factor of an inductor can be calculated using the following formula:

$$Q = \frac{\omega L}{R}$$

Where R is its internal resistance and ωL is the inductive reactance at a particular frequency.

By using an inductor with a ferromagnetic core a greater inductance can be achieved with using less coil turns and therefore less resistance thus having a greater Q factor.

8 DIODES

A diode, as explained previously, is simply a p-n junction.

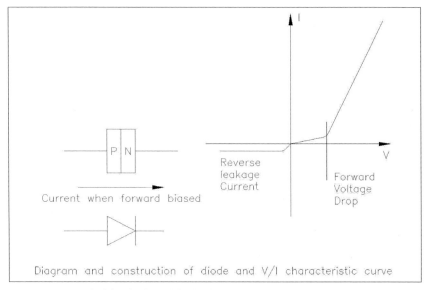

Diagram and construction of diode and V/I characteristic curve

p-n junction, symbol for diode and diode characteristic.

A semiconductor diode is similar to the thermionic valve diode in that it only allows electrons to flow in one direction. i.e. from the cathode toward the anode. It is therefore important to know which end is which!

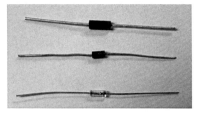

Various diodes.

The line on the diode will represent the cathode; other diodes will usually have a symbol printed on them denoting cathode and anode. Stud mounting diodes can be cathode or anode bodied so need to be checked against the manufacturer's data sheet if it is not obvious from the device markings.

Diodes fall mainly into two types: power and signal. Power diodes are used in power supplies to rectify alternating current (AC) to direct current (DC). They generally have to withstand high Voltages and carry large currents; as such they can be quite large and may require heat dissipation. However they are not generally required to switch very quickly (50 - 60Hz). Signal diodes are used as demodulators and logic elements and as such only have to deal with small voltages and small currents but may need to switch at very high speed (>Mhz). Signal diodes tend to be quite small devices.

Diodes can be made from germanium or silicon. Germanium diodes have a low forward Voltage drop, about 0.2 Volts, which lend themselves better to RF circuits whereas silicon diodes have a forward voltage drop of about 0.7 Volts. Germanium diodes will operate up to about 70°C and silicon diodes will operate up to about 200°C. The reverse leakage current is lower for a silicon diode (50nA) than for a germanium diode (1mA) and is therefore preferred for rectifier and logic applications.

When rating a diode, the forward voltage drop (0.7 V for a silicon diode) should be multiplied by the forward current to find the power dissipated as heat.

When selecting a diode for a particular purpose ensure that the current and peak inverse Voltage (PIV) will not be exceeded.

A useful diode for clamping, logic and op amp rectifiers is the 1N4148; these have a current rating of up to 100mA and a PIV of 75V.

For a lower forward Voltage drop (0.4 Volts at 10mA) with a fast switching time use a Shottky diode; the disadvantage of a Shottky diode is the low PIV and higher reverse leakage current.

Germanium diodes are preferred for radio circuits because of the low forward voltage drop, a typical diode would be the OA91.

A popular rectifier diode is the 1N4000 series up to 1A, or the 1N5000 series for 3A rating. The PIV for these series of diodes is indicated by the last digit.

> 1N4001 = 50V
> 1N4002 = 100V
> 1N4003 = 200V
> 1N4004 = 400V
> 1N4005 = 600V
> 1N4006 = 800V
> 1N4008 = 1000V

There are many other diodes available and their ratings will be listed in the manufacturers' data sheets and often in the suppliers' catalogues. Power diodes that have to work at much higher current carrying capacities may have heat sinks fitted or be stud mounted and will require suitable heat dissipation methods to operate at high power.

There are several variations of the simple diode and these are described below.

Bridge Rectifier

A bridge rectifier.

It is possible to connect four power diodes to create a full wave bridge rectifier and they are available in a single housing for power supplies. They can have current ratings in excess of 60A and PIV rating up to 1200V and they have built-in heat sinks. These are often found in power supplies, of which more information can be found in the relevant chapter.

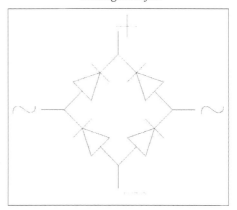

Diagram of bridge rectifier.

Zener diode

When a p-n junction is reverse-biased, a small amount of leakage current may still flow; normally this is negligible and can be ignored. However, if a large reverse biased voltage is applied the p-n junction will eventually 'avalanche'. This is a complex semiconductor effect where the normally minority carriers travel through the depletion layer and dislodge valence electrons causing a sudden and cumulative current flow. Normally, care is taken to ensure that this point is not reached by ensuring that the PIV (peak inverse Voltage) is not exceeded. However, by especially manufacturing the p-n junction with a deliberately low depletion layer, the point at which the avalanche effect occurs can be predictable and therefore useful. These diodes are called Zener diodes and will have a rated Voltage at which this breakdown occurs. Care has to be taken to limit the current through the Zener diode once it is conducting in the reverse-biased mode and it is normal therefore to have a resistor in series with the device to limit maximum current flow.

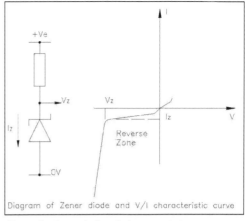

Diagram of Zener diode and V/I characteristic curve

The characteristics of the Zener diode make them useful as a Voltage reference device for power supplies and other circuits. However, Zener diodes can only dissipate a maximum of *Zener diode symbol and characteristic curve.* about 5 Watts and can produce a 'noisy' Voltage which may be a problem in audio and instrumentation amplifiers.

Varicap diode (varactor diode)

Varicap diode

Varicap symbol.

As previously explained, when a reverse biased Voltage is applied across a p-n junction, the depletion layer is increased. By varying the Voltage across the p-n junction, the width of the depletion layer can be varied. This varying depletion layer, in effect two conductors, separated by a varying insulator, behaves as a variable capacitor. A capacitance change from about 20pF to 40pF for a 5 Volt change in reverse bias is typical. Varicap diodes are widely used for electronic LC tuning circuits such as TV and radio tuners.

Generally, the depletion region thickness is proportional to the square root of the applied voltage; and capacitance is inversely proportional to the depletion region thickness. Thus, the capacitance is inversely proportional to the square root of applied voltage. All diodes exhibit this phenomenon to some degree, but specially made varicap diodes exploit the effect to boost the capacitance and variability range achieved.

9 THYRISTORS AND TRIACS/DIACS

Thyristor (SCR)

The thyristor (also called the Silicon-controlled Rectifier) is one of the main components in high Voltage and high current power electronics. It can be thought of as diode that is triggered using a gate signal into conducting. The trigger can be a very small pulse, microseconds, and very small Voltage and current but the thyristor will then conduct in the forward direction until power is either disconnected or reversed. This makes it particularly useful in AC dimmer circuits when the power does indeed reverse with the mains frequency. It is very important to ensure that the thyristors power rating is correct and its peak inverse Voltage (not the RMS Voltage in AC circuits) is not exceeded.

A thyristor.

The construction of a thyristor is akin to a semiconductor diode with four layers arranged as PNPN. They can then be thought of as an overlapping PNP transistor with an NPN transistor, which are connected by bases and the collector. Most thyristors are gated at the P layer and are referred to as a cathode gate (G_c) device and require a positive pulse to trigger. Some thyristors are gated at the N layer and are referred to as an anode gate (G_a) device and require a negative pulse to trigger. If

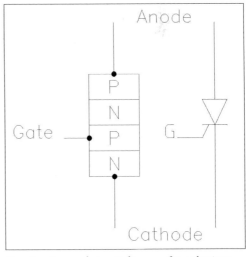

Construction and circuit diagram for a thyristor.

both gates are available it is called a thyristor tetrode, and one gate can switch the device on and the other gate can switch it off. Most thyristors, however, only have the three connectors and are called thyristor triodes and cannot be switched off by the gate signal.

A typical thyristor can conduct a current in excess of 50A with gate current of 20mA. It is possible to purchase thyristors that can handle currents in excess of 500A with a peak inverse Voltage (PIV) rating of 1600 Volts; this makes them useful for dimmer, motor and heater circuits.

Triac/Diac

A triac is constructed as two thyristors wired head-to-tail and it can therefore conduct in both directions (bi-directional), which is more efficient in AC circuits. The triac gets its name from 'triode alternating current switch'. They are available in the same three categories as thyristors and can be triggered by positive and negative pulses.

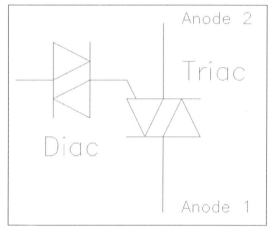

Diagram of Trac/Diac trigger circuit.

Triac circuits usually make use of a bi-directional trigger diode called a diac to fire the triac. Most diacs have similar characteristics with a trigger Voltage which when exceeded allows the diac to conduct freely. The triac and diac configuration is widely used in dimmer, motor and heater circuits.

10 TRANSISTORS

The transistor was invented by two American physicists in 1948 and the name comes from a combination of 'transfer' and 'resistance'. It is the most important component in electronics and can be used as an individual component or can be the basic element of an integrated circuit (IC).

Transistors.

There are several different types of transistor, and the main ones are listed here:

Bi-Polar Junction Transistor (BJT)
Field Effect Transistor (FET)
Metal Oxide Semiconductor Field Effect Transistor (MOSFET)
Unijunction Transistor (UJT)

Bi-Polar Junction Transistor

The bi-polar transistor is the most common type of transistor and is usually just referred to as a transistor, whereas the other types are more usually explicitly named. The bi-polar transistor is further sub-divided

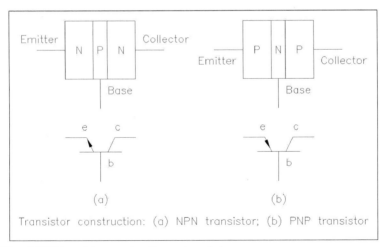

Transistor construction: (a) NPN transistor; (b) PNP transistor

NPN and PNP transistor construction and symbols.

into two basic types: the NPN transistor and the PNP transistor. The NPN transistor is made from two PN junctions sandwiched together (like two diodes back to back) such that it is a three-legged device where two legs are in each of the N-type materials and one leg is in the P type material. The PNP transistor is the opposite way around.

The N type and P type materials are made from germanium or more commonly silicon doped materials similar to the diode. The three legs of the transistor are called the emitter, base and collector. The emitter semiconductor material is heavily doped and the collector material is lightly doped with the middle (base) semiconductor material being relatively thin.

For an NPN transistor to operate the base voltage must be higher than the emitter voltage; this will allow electrons to flow from the emitter to the base setting up a small base current Ib. A germanium transistor will start to go into the forward-active region when the base is 0.2 Volts above the emitter and the silicon transistor will require about 0.7 Volts, just like a diode would. However, because the base region is so narrow, rather than leave the base they will immediately be attracted into the more highly charged collector region. Therefore a larger collector current Ic will flow.

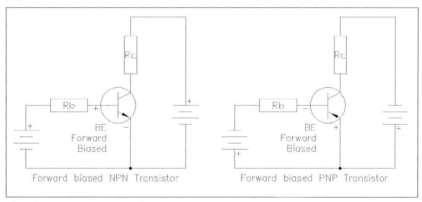

NPN and PNP transistors forward biased for operation.

This current gain is represented by h_{fe}; it is approximately the ratio of the collector current to the base current in forward-active region. It is typically greater than 100 for small-signal transistors but can be smaller in transistors designed for high-power applications.

Gain h$_{fe}$ = *Ic* / *Ib*

The ratio of *Ie/Ic* remains approximately constant at about 0.98 and is referred to as the common base gain α_F and is usually considered to be unity (1).

The structure of the transistor is such that the thin base region completely surrounds the emitter and the collector completely surrounds the base, such that the construction is not symmetrical. Small changes in the voltage applied across the base–emitter terminals causes the current that flows between the *emitter* and the *collector* to change significantly. This effect can be used to amplify the input voltage or current.

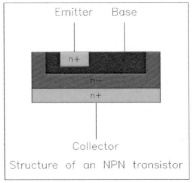

Need caption.

The PNP transistor operates similarly but requires the base voltage to be lower than the emitter voltage to be forward biased. For this reason NPN transistors are more common than PNP transistors.

The transistor operates in one of several ways: active, cut-off and saturated; there is also reverse-active but that is not in common use.

Active: that is when the base-emitter junction is forward biased and current is flowing between emitter and collector, the collector current flow is proportional to the base current but much greater.

Cut-off: that is when the base-emitter junction is reverse biased and no (or very little) current is flowing between the emitter and the collector. This is often used as an open (off) switch.

Saturated: that is when the base-emitter junction is fully forward biased and maximum current is flowing

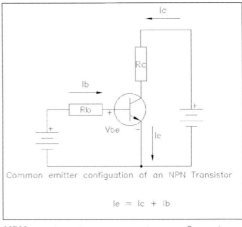

NPN transistor in common emitter configuration.

between the emitter and the collector. This is often used as a closed (on) switch.

The most common circuit configuration for a transistor is the common emitter amplifier. The base is used as the input, the collector as the output and the emitter is common to both.

A resistor can be put in the emitter connection to reduce current and thereby reduce gain but increase stability and linearity.

As the Voltage is increased to the base, current flow increases through the

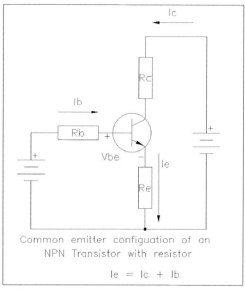

Common emitter configuation of an NPN Transistor with resistor

$$Ie = Ic + Ib$$

NPN transistor with series emitter resistor.

transistor from emitter to collector and hence through the resistor in the collector circuit. As the current flowing through the collector resistor increases, so the Voltage developed across it (Ohm's law) increases. If the Voltage across the collector resistor is increasing then the Voltage across the emitter-collector junction must be decreasing and therefore the potential measured at the collector with respect to the emitter is falling. Likewise, when the Voltage is decreased at the base the reverse is true. Therefore the Voltage signal at the base is both inverted and amplified at the collector.

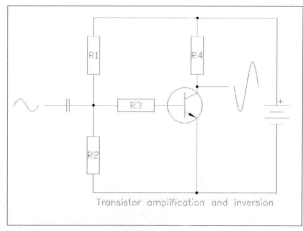

Transistor amplification and inversion

Signal inversion and amplification.

The common emitter amplifier can be used as a simple amplifier or as logic switch circuit. The input impedance of a transistor is relatively low at about 1KΩ and its output impedance is about 50KΩ.

Transistors can often be identified by the two letter and three numbers that are most commonly used to name them, e.g. BC108. The first letter will be either an A or a B and signifies the semiconductor material used; germanium or silicon respectively. The second letter signifies the area of use.

C   Low power for low frequency applications
D   Power for low frequency applications
F   Low power for high frequency applications
L   Power for high frequency applications
P   Phototransistor
S   Low power for switching applications
U   Power for switching applications

The remaining three digits identify the actual component; often adjacent numbering are similar transistors but one will be the NPN version and the other will be the PNP version. E.g. BD135 and BD136.

The other main characteristics of transistors that are often listed in manufacturers' data sheets and suppliers' catalogues and that should not be exceeded are:

Ic Collector current, this should never be exceeded.
P_{TOT} Total Power dissipation. This is equal to (Vce x Ic) + (Vbe x Ib).
V_{CEO} The reverse breakdown Voltage.
B, β or h_{fe} The current gain between collector current and base current.
f_T The transition frequency for which β is no longer in the region of 1

When selecting a transistor for a particular application all of the above factors should be taken into consideration.

Field Effect Transistor

Field effect transistors are similar to bi-polar transistors in respect of their base materials but function more like a controllable resistor. They are sub-divided into p channel type and n channel type devices. In some respects they resemble the triode thermionic valve in operation.

This is because the gate Voltage on a field effect transistor performs the same function as the grid on a thermionic valve.

Unlike the bi-polar transistor no current flows into the gate but it controls the width of the channel between the source and the drain, it therefore exhibits high input impedance that does not load the control source. There are two types of FET, the enrichment type and

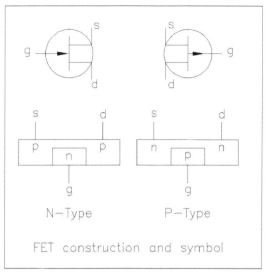

FET barrier layer and symbols.

the depletion type. The enrichment type is self blocking, because if the gate Voltage is unconnected or at 0 Volts with respect to the source then the channel will not conduct. The depletion type operates in the opposite manner, such that with no gate voltage the channel will be fully conducting. When a gate Voltage is applied of either polarity the drain current will reduce.

The gate connections are strongly doped but the channel material is weakly doped; this allows the gate Voltage to have a large influence on the barrier layer and hence the conductivity between the source and the drain.

Metal Oxide Semiconductor Field Effect Transistor

The Metal Oxide Semiconductor Field Effect Transistor or MOSFET is a variation of the Field Effect Transistor. The insulation between the gate and the channel is formed from a thin layer of silicon dioxide and the gate is a layer of aluminium. The conductive channel then becomes broader or narrower according to the Voltage applied at the gate. There are p channel, n channel, enrichment and depletion type MOSFETs and they exhibit high input impedance like a normal FET. MOSFETs are often used for high power switching from very small signal sources such as CMOS gate outputs. The MOSFET is sometimes called the Insulated Gate Field effect Transistor (IGFET) because the gate is insulated from the channel.

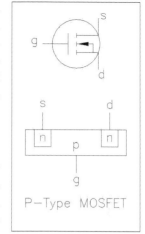

Uni-Junction Transistor

A uni-junction transistor (UJT) is a transistor that has only one junction. The UJT has three terminals: an emitter (E) and two bases (B1 and B2). The base is formed by lightly doped n-type bar of silicon that has two connections B1 and B2 at its ends. The emitter is of p-type and it is heavily doped. The resistance between B1 and B2, when the emitter is open-circuit is called the interbase resistance.

MOSFET and symbols.

The 2N2646 is the most commonly used version of the UJT.

It used to be used extensively for relaxation oscillators but since the introduction of the 555 timer is now mostly used to trigger thyristors in large AC current control circuits.

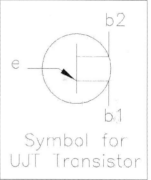

Diagram of UJT.

11 OP-AMPS

Op-Amps can be strung together in all sorts of ways to construct an analogue computer, widely used in measuring instruments and signal processing it can perform mathematical algorithms or 'operations', hence the name operational amplifier.

The Op-Amp as it is more commonly called is the ubiquitous analogue integrated circuit (IC). It is a high gain Voltage amplifier with a high impedance differential input and,

Example of an Op-Amp.

normally, a low impedance single ended output. Typically, it can produce a Voltage at its output many thousands of times the Voltage difference between its inputs. They are found in most analogue circuits such as motor controllers, audio circuits, filter circuits and instrumentation circuits. The Op-Amp can come in various packages but the most common is the 8 pin DIL (dual in line) as shown above. However they are available in dual and quad packages which save valuable circuit board space and power connections. They are also available in metal cans and even ceramic packages for high temperature applications.

There are literally hundreds of different op-amps available with slightly different characteristics, so for the purpose of this book, we shall examine the very popular µA741c, or just the 741 for short.

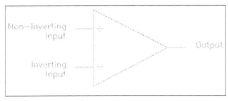

Op-Amp symbol.

The Op-Amp is represented by a simple triangle symbol with its differential inputs and its output; the power connections are often omitted (on the drawing not in real life!) because they are either assumed or not important for understanding the circuit. However, inside the 741 there are actually 20 transistors forming the high impedance differential input circuit, the high gain amplifier and a push-pull low impedance output with compensation for cross-over distortion that is able to drive a wide variety of loads up to several hundred milliWatts in power. The 741 has a gain of about 200000, an input impedance of 2MΩ and an output impedance of 75Ω. The + and – symbols at the inputs represent the non-inverting input and inverting inputs respectively; they do not represent the polarity of the inputs and should not be referred to as the positive and negative inputs.

The very high gain of an op-amp, usually between 10,000 and 1,000,000, and for a 741 it is quoted as 200,000 which is very approximate; therefore even a very small Voltage difference between the inputs would quickly drive the output Voltage to its rail Voltage and would saturate. This effect can be useful in the case of a comparator circuit but normally it is to be avoided. This can be done by using negative feedback; this where some of the output is fed back into the inverting input, the gain can then be precisely controlled. If some of the output was fed to the non-inverting input the feedback would be positive which generally leads to instability and unpredictable behaviour and is therefore to be avoided except in some type of oscillator circuits and a specific circuit called a Schmitt trigger.

When dealing with op-amps it is convenient to think of them as perfect devices, which of course they are not, but it helps with the maths! Firstly when an op-amp has negative feedback the Voltage between the inputs is reduced to zero, secondly because of the high input impedance they draw no current. In reality the 741 will draw a few nanoAmps and some op-amps with FET inputs only draw a few picoAmps.

The non-inverting amplifier

The non-inverting amplifier has its input signal that is to be amplified connected to the non-inverting input (+). The gain of the amplifier is determined by the potential divider of resistors R1 and R2 feeding some of the output back into the inverting input(-).

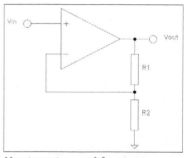

Non-inverting amplifier circuit.

$$Gain = 1 + \frac{R1}{R2}$$

So for example if R1 is 100kΩ and R2 is 10kΩ, the gain would be 11, in other words if there were a Voltage of say 0.5 Volts at the input there would be 5.5 Volts at the output. This might be a useful circuit for matching a sensors Voltage output to the analogue input of some test equipment for example.

The unity-gain buffer (Voltage follower)

If we took the non-inverting amplifier example above and made R1 a short circuit of 0Ω and R2 an open circuit of infinity ∞Ω, then the gain becomes one or unity.

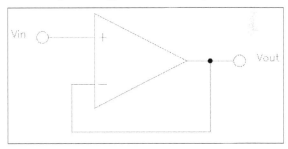

Unity gain-buffer.

$$Gain = 1 + \frac{R1}{R2} = 1 + \frac{0}{\infty} = 1$$

On the face of it this does not seem a very useful circuit, the output is the same as the input, but because of the input and output impedance properties of an op-amp, the output now exhibits low impedance. This makes this very useful for buffering Voltages sources that produce very little current such as microphones and photovoltaic cells; the Voltage is not amplified but its power is increased up to that of the op-amp. This circuit is so useful that some op-amps are ready built as buffers such as the LM310.

The inverting amplifier

The inverting amplifier as its name suggests will invert the input signal such that the output Voltage is of the opposite polarity.

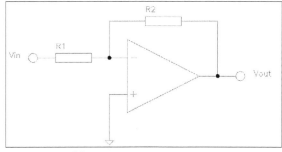

Inverting amplifier.

The inverting amplifier has its input signal that is to be amplified connected to the inverting input (-), the gain of the amplifier is again determined by the potential divider of resistors R1 and R2 feeding some of the output back into the inverting input (-).

$$Gain = \frac{-R2}{R1}$$

So for example if R1 is 10kΩ and R2 is 100kΩ, the gain would be -10; in other words if there were a Voltage of say 0.5 Volts at the input there would be -5 Volts at the output. This might be a useful circuit for matching a sensors Voltage output to the analogue input of some measuring equipment for example.

The Comparator

The op-amp comparator is a very useful circuit that can compare the Voltages present on the non-inverting input (+) and inverting input (-) and because there is no feedback will drive the output to either negative

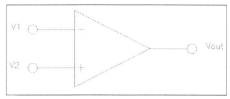

Diagram of the Comparator.

or positive saturation. The Voltage being measured must be within the limits of the device which is generally within the power supply range, whether bi-polar or uni-polar.

The output will go to positive saturation if the non-inverting input

(+) is greater than the inverting input (-). The output will go to negative saturation if the non-inverting input (+) is less than the inverting input (-).

+ > - = High

- > + = Low

The output of the comparator could, for example, be used to switch a transistor. Op-amp comparators are generally used as low performance comparators where speed is not critical. Where speed is critical there are dedicated comparator chips such as the LM339 that is designed to interface directly to digital logic and has much faster recovery and slew rates than a general purpose op-amp; however, the principle is the same.

Note: When a comparator performs the function of determining if an input voltage is above or below a given threshold, it is essentially performing a 1-bit quantization. This function is used in nearly all analog to digital converters in combination with other devices to achieve a multi-bit quantization.

The Difference (Differential) Amplifier

The difference amplifier, sometimes referred to as a differential amplifier (not to be confused with the differentiator) amplifies the difference between its input Voltages. Essentially the op-amp is operating as both an inverting amplifier and a non-inverting amplifier at the same time such that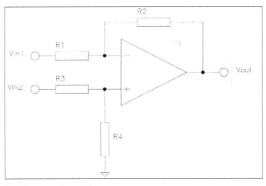

Difference Amplifier.

the output is the amplified difference of its inputs. It is normal, though not compulsory, to have equal gains for each of the gain circuits.

Where R2 = R4

$$Vout = \frac{R2 \times (Vin2 - Vin1)}{R1}$$

If all the resistors are of equal value then the equation is reduced to
Vout = V2 − V1
− and is then sometimes called a Subtractor circuit.

The Summing Amplifier

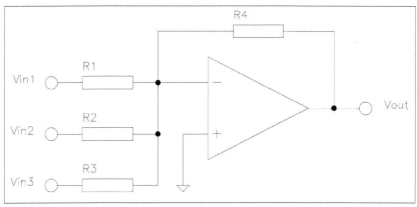

Diagram of the Summing Amplifier.

The summing amplifier will produce a negative sum of its inputs. Furthermore the individual inputs can be weighted such that the smaller the resistor the larger the weighting.

$$Vout = -R4 \left(\frac{Vin1}{R1} + \frac{Vin2}{R2} + \frac{Vin3}{R3} \right)$$

If all the resistors are of equal value the equation above reduces to

$$Vout = - (Vin1 + Vin2 + Vin3)$$

The circuit can be used as an audio mixer or it can be used to offset a Voltage. It can also be used to make a simple digital to analogue converter.

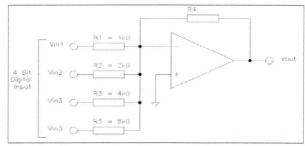

Diagram of simple D/A Converter.

Integrator

An op-amp integrator circuit will integrate the inverted input Voltage (Vin) over a given period of time, from 0 to t seconds with a scale factor of -1/RC.

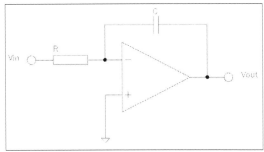

Diagram of Integrator.

Such that

$$Vout = - \frac{1}{RC} \int_0^t Vin\,dt + k$$

Where k is the starting value of Vout.

The integration is started by opening the switch and reset by closing it. This can be a manual switch or it can be done electronically with a JFET transistor with low input offset Voltage and low input current bias.

If Vin is constant and Vout is used to switch the JFET, perhaps by using a comparator or by using a timer, then assuming that Vout is 0V when t=0, a ramp generator can be designed such that

$$Vout = - \frac{Vint}{RC}$$

For example if $R = 10k\Omega$ and $C = 10\mu F$ and $t = 0.5s$ and Vin is constant at 0.1V then Vout will be 0.5V after 0.5s

Another use of the integrator is to integrate the changing value of a Voltage over time to obtain a mean value, eliminating short term variations.

Differentiator

An op-amp differentiator circuit will differentiate the inverted input Voltage (Vin) such that the output (Vout) depends on the rate of change of the input. This makes this a useful instrumentation circuit that can be used to convert, say, position to speed because speed is the rate of change of position and if the output of the first differentiator is fed to a second differentiator then the rate of change of speed will be the final result, i.e. acceleration.

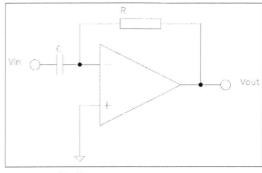

$Vout = -RC \times dVin / dt$

This is also a useful circuit for detecting short pulses, because even

Diagram of Differentiator.

a pulse with a relatively small duration can produce a relatively large output if the rate of change of Volts per second is quite large i.e. a spike. It can also be used as a high-pass filter circuit since AC signals with a higher frequency i.e. higher rate of change of Voltage will be amplified more than lower frequencies.

12 ANALOGUE ELECTRONICS

Analogue electronics (or analog in American English) are electronic systems where the Voltage or current signals vary in amplitude, unlike digital electronics where there are only two distinct Voltage levels. The meaning of 'analogue' is the proportional relationship between a signals amplitude and the real world signal that it is representing, e.g. speed. The word analogue is derived from the Greek word ανάλογος (analogos) meaning «proportional».

Real world information that continuously varies such as light, sound, temperature, pressure or speed can be converted by a transducer into a varying electrical signal; for example, a microphone changes sound into a varying Voltage. The louder the sound being picked up by the microphone the greater the Voltage or current produced by the microphone in proportion to the original waveform.

The signal could be any value from a given range, zero to ten Volts is a fairly common range of values used to represent many different analogue signals. So for example zero Volts could represent zero degrees Celsius and ten Volts could represent one hundred degrees Celsius; in such a system 2 Volts would represent 20 degrees Celsius.

Analogue electronic systems inherently include some noise, which are random variations caused at an atomic level within the electronic components or induced from nearby electromagnetic disturbances. As an analogue signal is amplified, filtered, manipulated and transmitted over a distance, the noisier it will become. A certain amount of diligence such as cable screening and using good quality components when designing analogue electronic equipment is required to help reduce the introduction and amplification of noise.

Analogue electronic circuits are generally more difficult to design and build than digital electronic circuits; which is one of the reasons why digital electronics is more popular. Digital electronics does not suffer with noise problems and analogue circuits cannot be programmed very easily. However, despite these drawbacks, analogue electronics is the only way to get real world proportional signals into and out of an electronic control system. Some analogue electronic circuits are completely analogue, for example an older transistor radio (not DAB) or an older hi-fi amplifier. However most electronic control systems that require an analogue interface to the real world do so by first converting from an analogue signal to a digital signal at the input where required and converting from a digital signal to an analogue signal at the output where required. For example a microphone will always be analogue as will a speaker but not necessarily all the electronics in between will be, especially if the recorded sound is to be stored on a CD or sent as an email for example.

Analogue to digital

Real world information such as temperature could be sensed by a temperature transducer and converted to a 0 to 10 Volt analogue signal representing 0 to 100 degrees Celsius using minimal analogue electronics, perhaps one or two Op-Amps would suffice. The 0 to 10 Volt analogue signal could then be converted to digital using an analogue-to-digital converter (ADC). An ADC converts the varying analogue signal into a varying series of binary numbers. Depending on how accurate the temperature control system needed to be would determine how many bits the ADC converts to. For a simple temperature control system an 8 bit ADC (which is 256 steps) would provide a resolution of 100/256 = 0.39 degrees per step, perfectly adequate for say cooking purposes but maybe not for NASA where a 10 bit (1024 steps, 0.097 degrees per step) or 12 bit (4096 steps, 0.0244 degrees per step) ADC may be required. Once the signal is in the digital domain it can be recorded, manipulated, sent from Mars and the information remains intact. The other consideration is how often the analogue signal is sampled; using the above example, a cooker may only sample once a second or less, NASA probably more often. The sampling rate for CD quality sound is every 22 microseconds at 16 bit (65536 steps).

An ADC circuit is made up of a number of Voltage comparators that turn on at successive Voltage levels that is then connected to a logic circuit that outputs the corresponding digital number as discrete binary outputs. This could be constructed with a resistor divider network, as many Op-Amp comparators as the output resolution requires and some combinational logic chips, however it is much easier to use a dedicated integrated circuit, IC, for the purpose.

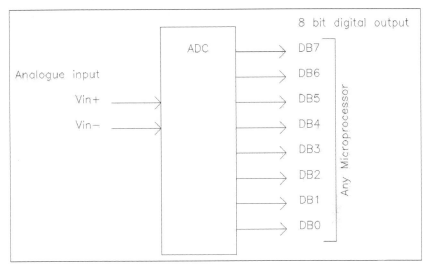

ADC chip.

Digital to analogue

Often it is necessary to convert digital information into an analogue signal so that it can be useful or understood by humans. An obvious example would be sound, especially if it has been stored, manipulated

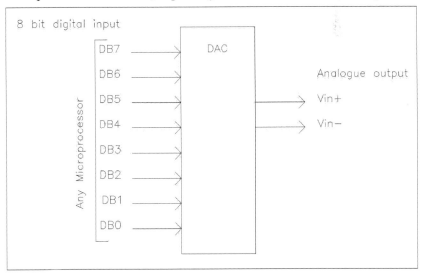

DAC chip.

or transmitted electronically such as a mobile phone or VoIP. A digital-to-analogue converter (DAC) converts a digital signal into an analogue signal; in the mobile phone example this signal would then be amplified and drive a small loudspeaker. There are several different types of DAC depending on the particular application but again like the ADC they are readily available as integrated circuits. A DAC in a music player would be relatively low speed high resolution where as a DAC in a video circuit would be very high speed but relatively low resolution. The DAC would sample the digital signal and output a Voltage corresponding to the binary number. A simple low resolution DAC might be 8 bit with a slow clocked sampling rate and a higher resolution DAC might be 16 or even 24 bit with a very fast sampling rate.

Another area of analogue electronics is the amplifier but that will be given its own chapter.

13 AMPLIFIERS

An amplifier is an electronic device that amplifies (increases) the power of a signal. The best known example of an amplifier is an audio power amplifier but there are other types of amplifiers such as RF (radio frequency) amplifiers, servo motor amplifiers and specialised microwave amplifiers for radar.

All the above amplifiers take energy from its power supply and controls its output to follow the waveform of the input signal but with a larger amplitude. There are four types of electronic amplifier: Voltage amplifier, current amplifier, transconductance amplifier and transresistance amplifier. By far the most common type of amplifier is the Voltage amplifier which is used mainly for audio and RF purposes. The current amplifier is mainly used for motor control purposes and the other two are for more specialised purposes. We shall limit ourselves to the Voltage amplifier.

Amplifiers can be constructed from Op-Amps, discrete transistors or thermionic valves or a combination of any of these. Although thermionic valves are very old technology they are still favoured by some for electric guitar amplification and by some audiophiles; they are also used for microwave amplification (klystron, travelling wave tube) in radar applications. Op-Amps have been covered in another chapter, however, it is quite possible and quite common for an Op-Amp electronic pre-amplifier circuit to feed a higher powered transistor amplifier.

Transistor amplifiers can be constructed from bipolar junction transistors (BJT) and metal oxide semiconductor field effect transistors (MOSFET). The BJT or more commonly just called a transistor amplifier can be configured as *common base, common collector* or *common emitter* amplifier and the MOSFET can be configured as *common gate, common source* or *common drain* amplifier. Each configuration of both types of transistor have different characteristics such as gain and impedance.

An audio amplifier is normally used to amplify music or speech. It might be a pre-amplifier (preamp) which may include filters and tonal control or might be a power amplifier that drives loudspeakers directly. The input impedance of the audio pre-amplifier needs to match either

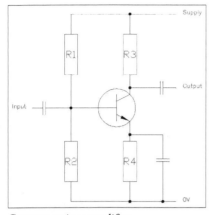

Common emitter amplifier.

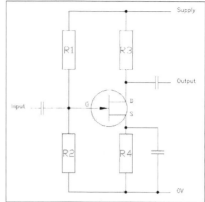

Common source amplifier.

a microphone, the output of another amplifier or perhaps a musical instrument such as a guitar. The output impedance of the audio amplifier has to match the speakers or the input of another amplifier or some other audio equipment. The frequency response needs to match that of the human ear, 20 Hz to 20 kHz and needs to be fairly linear over the whole range so that the human ear does not detect variations. The power output from the power amplifier needs to be sufficient to drive the loudspeaker without too much distortion. There will always be some distortion but the aim is to design an amplifier where the distortion is within acceptable limits for the human ear, except perhaps for some occasional guitar distortion where it is deliberate (blame Jimi Hendrix).

Power amplifier classes

There are several classes of amplifier: class A, B, AB, C, D, E, G, H and more. Class A used to be the holy grail of audio amplifier design since the amplifier is always biased on and there is no cross-over distortion as the signal passes through the zero point which

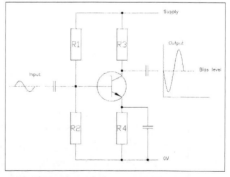

Circuit diagram of class A amplifier and waveform.

reduces odd harmonic distortion. However the class A amplifier is very inefficient (less than 50%) and requires a large heat sink to dissipate all the wasted energy. It is still used by hobbyists for its simplicity and audiophiles for its superior sound quality; but other more efficient designs are more generally used.

A Class B amplifier only amplifies half the input waveform and is often used in cheap radios and for computer audio, however if two B class amplifiers are designed in a push-pull arrangement then the whole signal is amplified except for a small dead band around the zero point which leads to a small amount of cross-over distortion. They are however much more efficient.

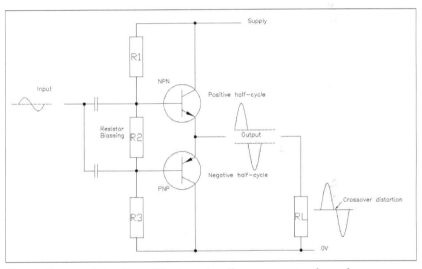

Circuit diagram of class B amplifier in push-pull arrangement and waveform.

An improvement on this design is to bias the class B push-pull arrangement with diodes with a fixed 0.7V bias so that they overlap slightly at the cross-over point. This reduces the cross-over distortion and decreases the efficiency slightly and is known as the Class AB amplifier. This is the most common form of audio amplifier nowadays.

The Class C amplifier only amplifies half the input signal but is very efficient; it is normally used in RF applications to amplify a carrier signal. The class D (not digital) amplifier is more accurately a fast switch and is used in pulse width modulation (PWM) applications such as driving

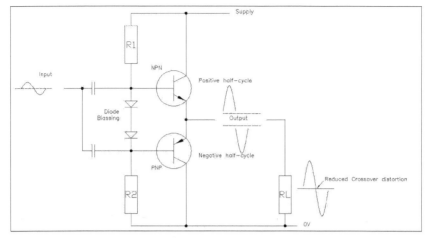

Circuit diagram of class AB amplifier and waveform.

servo and stepper motors, although lately it has been used for some very efficient sub-woofer designs. The other classes of amplifier are more specialised and beyond the scope of this book.

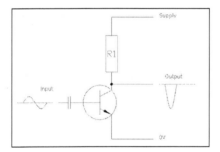

Circuit diagram of class C amplifier and waveform..

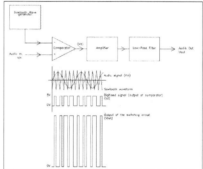

Block diagram of class D amplifier and waveforms

14 LOUDSPEAKERS

A loudspeaker (or speaker) is a transducer that converts an electrical signal into sound. Loudspeakers are used in many applications such as telephones, audio systems, broadcasting and in many types of music players. Larger loudspeakers are used in theatres and concerts for sound reinforcement.

A typical loudspeaker.

The most common type of loudspeaker is the dynamic loudspeaker that uses a lightweight diaphragm connected loosely to a frame. The centre of the diaphragm has a copper coil that is inside a cylindrical magnet such that when an electrical signal is applied to the coil it moves backwards and forwards inside the magnetic field. This movement is directly connected to the diaphragm thereby producing sound waves in air.

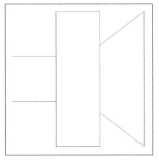

Symbol for loudspeaker.

Loudspeaker enclosure terminals are often marked + and – or 'red' and 'black' although it does not actually matter which way around the speaker is connected to the source of the signal. However, if you have more than one speaker in a system they should all be connected the same way around. This is so as not to have sound waves out of phase with each other and cancelling each other out. However, no damage will occur if it is wrong.

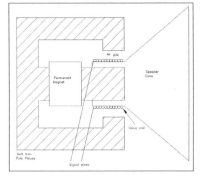

Diagram of louspeaker construction.

Speaker specifications

Speaker specifications normally include the driver type, rated power and impedance.

Driver types are full-range, woofer, mid-range or tweeter.

The rated power is usually given as two values, continuous and peak which, as their titles indicate, is the power that they can handle continuously or a maximum short-term blast. A speaker should be selected so that it is working comfortably within its rated capability. The rating is always given in Watts.

The impedance of a loudspeaker is usually given as 4Ω or 8Ω (Ohms). This impedance value is a nominal value because the impedance will change with the frequency of the source signal however it is 1.15 times the minimum impedance value. It is important to match the impedance of a loudspeaker to its signal source because it will determine the amount of current drawn from the amplifier. If an 8 Ohm speaker is connected to an amplifier with an output impedance of 4 Ohms then there will be a very noticeable drop in sound level. If a 4 Ohm speaker is connected to an amplifier with an 8 Ohm output then it may well damage the amplifier because it will draw twice as much current as the amplifier was designed to deliver. It is possible to connect multiple loudspeakers in series and parallel to achieve the desired impedance. For example two 4 Ohm speakers in series will have a total impedance of 8 Ohms and two 8 Ohm speakers in parallel with have a total impedance of 4 Ohms.

Most loudspeakers are designed to work with as wide a frequency response as possible such that only one speaker or driver is required. Such uses would be for small radios and televisions, public address systems, intercoms and some computer systems. These are called full-range loudspeakers.

However, loudspeakers are often placed within an enclosure and may have several individual drivers. These drivers being:

subwoofers	very low frequencies
woofers	low frequencies
mid-range	middle frequencies
tweeters	high frequencies

The high frequencies, middle frequencies and low frequencies have to be separated from each other and connected to their relevant drivers. This is accomplished with a *crossover*. A crossover can be either passive or active. A passive crossover is simply a Butterworth band-pass filter circuit made up of capacitors, resistors and inductors that are tuned to their relevant frequencies. A passive filter does not require any external power and is often inside the loudspeaker enclosure. They are quite popular for home hi-fi systems.

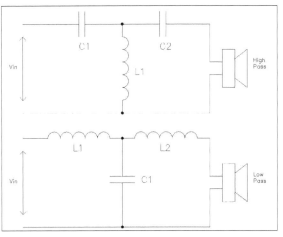

A third order (18dB/Octave) passive Butterworth high-pass and low pass filter.

They operate at the power amplifiers output and so therefore do not introduce much noise. A high quality passive crossover can be quite expensive because the resistors, capacitors and inductors in the filters have to be able to withstand the Voltages and currents at the power amplifers output. The disadvantage is that the frequency response cannot be easily altered.

The active crossover circuit typically uses op-amps with tuned circuits in their feedback path to alter their gain at specific frequencies. This gives them the advantage that their gains at different frequencies can be adjusted. However, this gives them the disadvantage that the filtering has to be done at pre-amplifier levels which means that the noise introduced by the op-amps is amplified

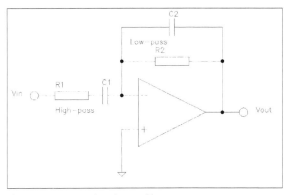

An active op-amp band-pass filter.

by the power amplifiers. This also means that there is a separate power amplifier for each output band.

The advantage of an active crossover is better isolation of each of the bands which produces less inter-modulation, distortion and overdriving. The power amplifier power requirement is also reduced quite significantly because no energy is lost in the passive components.

An active crossover can also be implemented digitally using a DSP (digital signal processor) which is a type of microprocessor that uses an analogue-to-digital converter to digitise the sound signal and then manipulate the signal before converting it back to analogue again. This has the advantage of not introducing noise and of being able to program and memorise frequency response.

There are several other types of loudspeakers but most are not in common use except for the piezoelectric speaker that is often used for single frequency applications such as beepers in watches and other electronic devices. They do however have the advantage of being quite resistant to overload that would destroy a conventional dynamic loudspeaker.

15 MICROPHONES

A microphone is a transducer that converts sound into an electrical signal. Microphones are used in many applications such as telephones, audio systems, broadcasting and in computers for speech recognition and VoIP. There are several different types of microphones including

A typical dynamic vocal microphone.

dynamic, condenser, piezoelectric, fibre optic and laser microphones. The most common type of microphone used in the entertainment industry is the dynamic microphone which uses electromagnetic induction to convert sound into an electrical signal.

A dynamic microphone works like a loudspeaker in reverse. A small moveable inductor coil is attached to a diaphragm and is positioned in the magnetic field of a permanent magnet. When sound waves vibrate the diaphragm the attached coil will produce a small current due to electromagnetic induction. Magnetic coil pick-ups on electric guitars use the same principle.

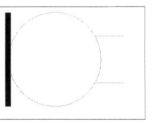

Electronic symbol for a microphone.

Most microphones found in the entertainment industry have a low impedance (under 200Ω). This is because a high impedance microphone with a long cable would result in high frequency signal loss due to cable capacitance and they tend to pick up more hum and interference. It is advisable to match the output impedance of a microphone to the input impedance of the amplifier that it will be connected to. No damage will occur if it is not 'matched' but there will be a loss of signal if it is not matched. It is however possible to use a line matching transformer to convert a microphones impedance for matching to high impedance equipment such as valve amplifiers.

A dynamic microphone can be connected to an op-amp to create a reasonable quality microphone preamplifier. Operational amplifiers have fast slewing rate and low noise characteristics that make them ideal for microphone amplifiers.

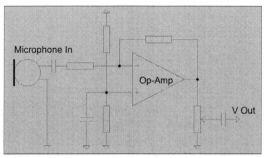

Circuit diagram of a simple microphone preamplifier using an op-amp.

16 BOOLEAN LOGIC

Boolean logic is used extensively in digital electronics; it is a mathematical subarea of Boolean algebra which in itself is a subarea of algebra.

Boolean logic is a mathematical subject that deals with true or false values. The true value is usually denoted by a '1' and the false value is usually denoted by a '0'. Boolean logic is fundamental to the understanding of digital electronics. It was originally introduced by George Boole in his 1847 book *The Mathematical Analysis of Logic*. The basic operations of Boolean logic are:

AND (x AND y) (Both inputs must be true for the output to be true).

OR (x OR y) (One input, or the other input or both inputs must be true for the output to be true).

XOR Exclusive OR (x XOR y) (One input, or the other but not both inputs must be true for the output to be true).

NOT (NOT x) (It takes only one input (unary operator) and the output is the negated input).

NAND (NOT AND) (x NAND y) (One input only must be true for the output to be true).

NOR (NOT OR) (x NOR y) (Both inputs must be false for the output to be true).

XNOR (Exclusive NOT OR) (x XNOR y) (Both inputs must be false or both true for the output to be true).

X	Y	AND	OR	XOR	NAND	NOR	XNOR	NOT
0	0	0	0	0	1	1	1	
0	1	0	1	1	1	0	0	
1	0	0	1	1	1	0	0	
1	1	1	1	0	0	0	1	
1	—							0
0	—							1

Boolean truth table.

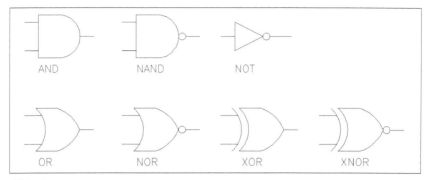

All logic gates.

A switch can only be in one of two states, on (True) or off (False), hence the use of Boolean logic to manipulate binary (base 2) information. Two switches in series can be thought of as an AND circuit since both switches would need to be on to allow a current to pass through. Two switches in parallel can be thought of as OR circuit since either switch will allow the current to pass.

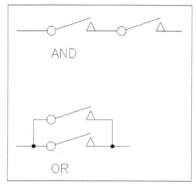

Switches arranged as an AND and OR circuit.

A complex logic gate is made up of a number of logic gates to perform a specific function. The diagram (right) has three gates and three inputs and eight possible outcomes.

The circuit could be written as Z = D OR E, or Z = NOT (A) OR (B AND C)

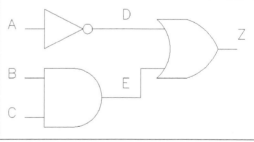

A complex logic gate.

A full adder circuit uses two XOR gates and two AND gates and an OR gate. Although both these gates could be constructed with two transistors each generally a CMOS IC will use at least four transistors for each gate. Therefore one adder circuit would need 25 transistors.

A	B	C	D	E	Z
0	0	0	1	0	1
0	0	1	1	0	1
0	1	0	1	0	1
0	1	1	1	1	1
1	0	0	0	0	0
1	0	1	0	0	0
1	1	0	0	0	0
1	1	1	0	1	1

Truth table of complex logic gate.

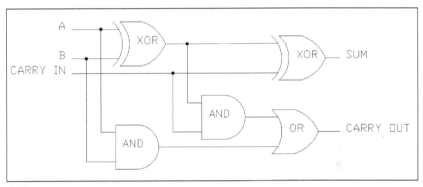

Adder circuit.

This adder is capable of adding $1 + 2 = 3_{10}$ (denary) or $10 + 1 = 11_2$ in binary. To add bigger numbers requires more adders. A microprocessor that is capable of dealing with numbers up to 4294967295 (32 bit unsigned integer) requires an enormous amount of adders. The Arithmetic Logic Unit (ALU) in a CPU (Central Processing Unit) is built from millions of transistors arranged as a combinational digital electronic circuit allowing just such additions.

Boolean logic is also used in nearly every programming language.

17 DIGITAL ELECTRONICS

Digital electronics almost universally represents signals as one of two states: on or off. This is often represented as true or false or as '1' or '0'. This simple fact makes digital electronics a very efficient method of manipulating and storing data and is almost immune from parasitic noise, attenuation or manufacturing tolerance. The two states are normally represented by two Voltage levels, the '0' level is normally at or near 0 Volts and the '1' state is at or near the supply Voltage. Typically, for example, if the supply Voltage is 5 Volts then a '1' state would be any Voltage above about 3.5 Volts and a '0' state would be anything below about 1.5 Volts. This allows the digital circuit quite a wide tolerance of Voltage levels before the state becomes ambiguous.

This high tolerance of Voltage levels mean that it is relatively easy to switch an electronic device into one of the two states. Digital circuits are then made up of a large number of logic gates each carrying out a simple Boolean logic function such that very complex electronic circuits can be achieved. For example, an analogue audio signal can be represented by a series of very fast changing numbers representing the audio amplitude as a 16 bit (16 on and off switches) number. A compact disc does exactly that by changing the audio signal level every 22 microseconds. This data can then be stored, manipulated, sent by email across the planet with no loss of information and thus the audio signal can be recovered by more digital electronics perfectly.

In addition, digital circuits are much more easily controlled by software, because software is also made up of '1's and '0's. Therefore transferring software data into and out of digital electronics is relatively straightforward such that a digital electronic device can be programmed and re-programmed to perform many different functions without changing the hardware. The noise immunity of using two simple states to represent data applies to the software data too so that complex instructions and complex hardware can be used together reliably to realise all kinds digital electronic equipment.

A simple digital circuit may take its information from the real world as an on or off signal, say a pushbutton and it may give its output as an on or off signal, say a light bulb, in which case the digital circuit might be very simple with only one or two logic gates. However, most digital circuits are very complex with hundreds, thousands, millions or billions of logic gates. The laptop I'm writing this on has a processor with 1.4 billion logic gates.

Each logic gate performs a very simple Boolean logic function, e.g. AND, OR, NOT, NAND, NOR, XOR, XNOR but when many logic gates are combined a combinational logic circuit is created. This might be a fixed logic circuit that always performs the same task or it might be more complex where either the logic circuit itself is programmable, known as a programmable logic device PLD or that the logic circuit can respond to software commands. Integrated circuits, IC, are the easiest way to make logic circuits; there are many different types of integrated circuits that can perform all manner of combined logic functions that can be further combined to create the precise electronic circuit required. A programmable logic device, PLD, is as its name suggests a device where the combined logic can be programmed and edited to suit the application. Although the PLD is likely to be more complex than if it were constructed from separate dedicated ICs, the overall cost will be much lower and take up less circuit board space and power consumption and it also has the advantage that it can be re-programmed if the requirement changes. When the logic requires complex algorithms, sequences or variable memory then a small microcontroller can be used to make an embedded system. The embedded system hardware is far more complex but can be used to perform quite complicated tasks that have to be programmed by a software engineer. The microcontroller could be a relatively simple PIC (originally Peripheral Interface Controller) that can perform modest programmable tasks using an Assembler or C compiler. Alternatively the microcontroller could be a very advanced device capable of many instructions with all sorts of dedicated functions. Again this could be programmed using an Assembler, C, or a dedicated microprocessor compiler.

A PIC.

A programmable logic controller PLC is another programmable logic device which originally took the place of many relays that were hardwired to carry out a particular logic function. Nowadays a PLC is capable of far more functions with interfaces for serial communications, motion control, analogue signal conversion, etc. They are usually programmed using a logic language called 'ladder' that replicates the way the original relay circuits were hardwired.

When creating a simple logic circuit, a truth table is used. This lists all the inputs and the outputs of the logic circuit and the required state of the outputs depending on all the possible *A PLC.* combinations of the inputs. This truth table is then translated into a Boolean expression which may then require simplifying using a Karnaugh map. The resultant Boolean expression is then mimicked using a combination of logic gates. This type of circuit would be useful for an electronic circuit that always behaves the same. Often it is required to use one or more of the outputs and feed it back into the system as an input; the logic circuit then becomes a sequential circuit. This makes the system quite a lot more difficult to design as the behaviour of the circuit becomes a sequence. Luckily, there are software design tools that can help with the design of sequential logic. The simplest sequential logic circuit is a 'flip-flop' or latch which changes its output state every time the input state goes from '0' to '1'. The flip-flop can therefore be used to remember state information as a storage element. It can also be used for counting pulses and for synchronising variably timed input pulses to a common clock signal.

There are several types of flip-flops, the simple set-reset latch, the T (toggle), the JK latch and the D flip-flop. They are all available as integrated circuits with usually several latches on one chip.

Sequential circuits can be either synchronous or asynchronous. A

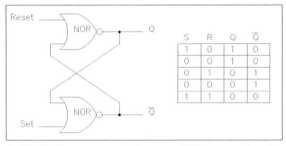

An SR flip flop constructed from two NOR gates and truth table.

synchronous system has a clock pulse such that all states of the circuit change at the same time on receiving the same clock pulse. The speed of the clock signal cannot be allowed to exceed the slowest logic calculation. An asynchronous sequential logic circuit does not have a clock pulse which means that all possible logic states have to be considered which can make a circuit unstable if not properly designed. However, the speed of an asynchronous circuit is only limited by the maximum speed of its logic gates.

A group of flip-flops is called a register and it is possible then to have a bus that can carry the result of a register calculation to other parts of the system. The control unit of a microprocessor is made up of a number of registers that are then sequenced using a count address derived from combinational logic. The computer is therefore a collection of simpler logic systems. Almost all computers are synchronous although there a few rare exceptions.

Logic families

Early logic circuits were made with relays and later with vacuum valves; these early circuits were slow, unreliable and used a lot of power. It was not until the invention of transistors that semiconductor logic families emerged. The first logic family was the resistor-transistor logic family and then the diode-transistor logic (DTL) family. It was the advent of the transistor-transistor logic (TTL) that was a great improvement of speed, reliability and fanout (the number of other logic devices that can be connected to its output) that integrated circuits became powerful. TTL logic is still used (7400 series) but the most common logic family in use now is the CMOS (Complementary Metal Oxide Semiconductor) family which is very fast, low power and has high noise immunity. The CMOS logic gates uses complementary and symmetrical pairs of p-type and n-type MOSFETs. The first family of CMOS logic integrated circuits was the 4000 series. Early TTL ICs required a 5 Volt power supply but early CMOS ICs could work from a 3 Volt to 15 Volt supply which made

A 74 series chip.

interfacing the two families together awkward because the two families were using different Voltage levels to represent '1' and '0'. This problem was solved with the emergence of the 74HCT family which combined CMOS technology with TTL switching levels.

Logic gate

A single logic gate will perform a single Boolean function, which means it will take in its inputs and produce a single logical output. The basic Boolean logic gates are AND, OR and NOT. There are then the negative versions of the AND and OR gate which is the NAND and NOR gate respectively. In addition there is the exclusive OR gate which is the XOR gate and its negative equivalent the XNOR gate.

Some gates have an additional third state to the two output states, '1' or '0', high Voltage or low Voltage, known as the tristate where the output is high impedance, i.e. as if it were disconnected. In this state the output of the gate plays no part in any logic gates that are connected to its output. The output of multiple registers onto a bus can thus be multiplexed allowing multiple chips to send data to a single control circuit.

18 555 TIMER

The 555 timer IC is so useful that it deserves a mention of its own. It is an integrated circuit that can be used as a timer, pulse generator, oscillator and flip-flop. It has been around since 1971 but is still in widespread use due to its ease of use, stability and low price. It is now made by many companies

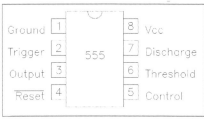

Pinout of 555 timer.

both in its original bi-polar transistor form and in the low power CMOS form. It is estimated that a billion 555 chips are manufactured every year. The original 555 chip had a single timer but there are now dual (556) and quad (558) timer versions.

The 555 has three modes of use: monostable (one shot), astable (free-running) and bistable (flip-flop) mode.

Monostable

In monostable mode the 555 functions as a 'one shot' pulse generator when triggered. Applications include timers, missing pulse detection, bounce-free switches, frequency divider and pulse width measurement (PWM). The pulse is triggered when the tigger input falls below a

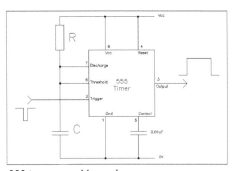

555 in monostable mode.

third of the supply Voltage. The width of the pulse is determined by an RC network and is given by

t = 1.1RC where t is in seconds, R is in Ohms and C is in Farads.

Astable

In astable mode the 555 operates as an oscillator and gives out a constant stream of pulses at a specified frequency and mark/space ratio. Applications include flashing circuits, pulse generation, logic clocks, tone generation and pulse position modulation. If a sensor that changes its resistance e.g. a thermistor or light dependent resistor is used as one of the timing resistors then a microprocessor or PIC can be programmed to measure the change in running frequency and respond accordingly. In astable mode the frequency of the pulse stream is determined by R1, R2 and C and is given by

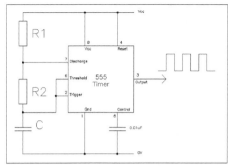

555 in astable mode.

$$f = 1.44/(R_1 + 2R_2)C$$

The high time is given by

$$\text{high } t = 1.44 * (R_1 + R_2)C$$

The low time is given by

$$\text{low } t = 1.44 * R_2C$$

Bistable

In bistable mode the 555 acts as a flip-flop. Applications include bounce-free latched switches and simple memory latch.

There are no timing components when used as a bistable, instead the discharge pin is left open circuit so that it retains its state indefinitely (whilst powered). Pulling the

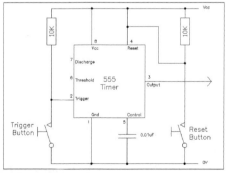

555 in bistable mode.

trigger to ground will set the output high: pulling the reset pin to ground will set the output low.

There are plenty of online calculators and simulators to help with determining the resistor and capacitor values as well as of lots of circuits to look at.

19 MICROPROCESSORS

The subject of microprocessors is huge and to cover it adequately would require a book of its own, therefore this chapter is an introduction to microprocessors as no book on electronics would be complete without it.

A microprocessor.

A microprocessor is a multi-purpose programmable device that accepts digital data as its input and then processes that data according to a set of sequential instructions stored in its memory and then provides its results as digital outputs.

Microprocessors can be found in personal computers but they can also be found in embedded systems providing digital control for household appliances, toys, hi-fi, cars, mobile phones, industrial process control and a whole plethora of other devices.

There are many different designs of microprocessors from the relatively simple and slow 4 bit processors of the early 70s right up to the very fast multi core 64 bit processors available today. The internal structure of a microprocessor is extremely complex, made from a few thousand transistors in the early 4 bit processors to millions of transistors in a single *integrated circuit* for the most modern processors. However, the major components that are found in all microprocessors are:

- A control unit
- An arithmetic-logic unit (ALU)
- Several registers

The *control unit* executes the instructions in the program sequentially and controls events inside and outside the processor. It does this extremely quickly; a modern processor is able to execute instructions at a rate well in excess of a billion every second.

The *arithmetic-logic unit* (ALU) is where the arithmetic and logic operations are carried out. The tasks an ALU can carry out therefore are to add, subtract binary numbers in the registers and to carry out logic instructions such as AND and OR. The control unit controls the ALU so it

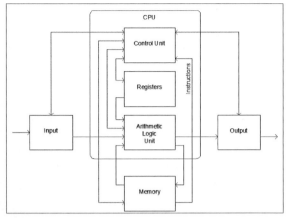

The main components of a processor.

knows when to perform any particular instruction. An ALU has two data input registers that is as wide as the number of bits in the word, e.g. 8 bit, 16 bit, 32 bit or 64 bit; it has a data output, control input and control output.

For example, if it is to add two numbers, then it is the task of the control unit to present the two numbers to the two ALU data inputs, then instruct the ALU to add the numbers. The result will then be at the ALU data output and it will again be the task of the control unit to transfer the result to the desired destination, whether that is a digital output, an area of memory or one of the microprocessors own registers. If the addition of three numbers is required the processor will first add two of the numbers together, put the result in an internal register and then add the third number.

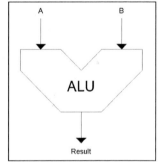

The symbol for an ALU.

A *register* is the name given to a storage element within the processor. Each register can hold one data word only and has one data input, one data output and one control input. When data is written to a register it overwrites whatever data was previously there, but when data is read from a register its contents remain unchanged. The task of the control unit is to ensure that the correct data word is present on the data bus at the registers data input and then send a control signal to the register to tell the register to open its data input so that the data word is copied in. Most microprocessors have eight, 16 or 32 registers. The number of internal registers has a significant impact on the efficiency of instruction code. There are a number of special registers such as the instruction pointer (program counter) that stores the memory address of the next instruction. When a processor is first booted up the instruction pointer normally looks at memory address zero for its first instruction.

Architecture

Computer *architecture* refers to the way that the processor and the main memory are connected. There are two possible architectures: the von Neumann and the Harvard.

The von Neumann architecture connects the processor and the main memory on one set of buses, the address bus, data bus and control bus.

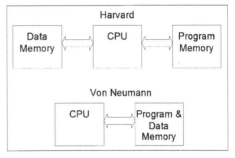

The von Neumann and the Harvard architectures.

The Harvard architecture connects the processor to two separate memory areas: the program memory and the data memory. In a von Neumann architecture care has to be taken not to overwrite other data in the main memory even though both computer instructions and data memory are travelling along the same buses. This can lead to severe congestion known as a 'bus bottleneck'. The alternative Harvard architecture uses two physically separate memories, one to hold the program and one to hold the data that the program is operating on. Each of the memories has its own address bus, data bus and control bus. In a Harvard architecture, a location in data memory can have the same address as a location in program memory but no confusion occurs because the address signals are sent along two physically separate address buses. The great advantage is that there are two data buses that alleviate the 'bus bottleneck' problem.

Instructions

All processors have a set of simple instructions that they are able to perform on binary data. Different processors have different *instruction sets* depending on the sort of tasks that they have been designed for; some of the instructions will be quite special and protected by patents, however there are some very common instructions that nearly all processors have. There are three types of instructions, these being:

- arithmetic/logic instructions
- data move instructions
- control instructions

Arithmetic and logic instructions would typically include add, subtract, AND and OR. Move instructions move data around without changing it, for example they might move data from the main memory to the processors registers or vica-versa, or from the processors registers to the output sub-systems or from one register to another. Control instructions can alter the order in which the instructions are carried out, perhaps in response to the result of a calculation or a special condition has been met. Typically these might be 'jump absolute', jump relative', 'jump if negative relative'. It does this by changing the value of the instruction pointer.

The instructions and data at machine level are in binary format, although usually shortened into hexadecimal notation which is not very easy for humans to follow. Therefore code is written in *assembly language* which is lot easier to understand and once translated into machine code is very efficient.

An example of assembly language is as follows:

```
load direct r1 0205
load direct r2 0206
subtract register r2 r1 r8
jump if negative relative 0002
stop
```

In this example the value held at memory location 0205 is loaded into register r1 and the value held at memory location 0206 is loaded into register r2. The value of register r1 is then subtracted from the value of the contents of register r2 and the result is placed in r8. The program will then jump two places if the result of that subtraction is negative, if the result is positive the program will not jump and will therefore execute the stop instruction.

The equivalent machine code might look as follows (depending on the actual processor):

Instruction step (Hex)	Program content (Hex)	Assembly instruction
0000	E10205	load direct r1 0205
0001	E20206	load direct r2 0206
0002	030218	subtract register r2 r1 r8
0003	830002	jump if negative relative 0002
0004	880000	stop

In binary it looks like this (!):

0000	1110 0001 0000 0010 0000 0101
0001	1110 0010 0000 0010 0000 0110
0010	0000 0011 0000 0010 0001 1000
0011	1000 0011 0000 0000 0000 0010
0100	1000 1000 0000 0000 0000 0000

High level languages

Programming in assembly language can be quite tedious for even the simplest applications, so it is more common to program the processor in a high level language such as C. This removes the programmer from having to know exactly which instructions, registers or even which memory locations that the processor will use. Instead the programmer will deal with higher concepts such as variables, arrays, objects, complex arithmetic or Boolean expressions, subroutines, functions, loops and other abstract computer concepts. This allows the programmer to concentrate on usability over optimal program efficiency. The upside is that complex coding is much easier and the downside is that the eventual machine code will be less efficient. A program written in a high level language will require *compiling* into the lower level machine code. It would also be true to say that very few programmers could actually produce machine code than is more efficient than a compiled high level code for complex programs.

Using the example given earlier, a high level equivalent piece of code might look as follows:

```
00      a = b - c
10      If a < 0 Then Goto 30
20      Else End
30
```

Where a, b and c are variables and 30 is a location in the program.

20 QUARTZ CRYSTAL OSCILLATOR

Quartz is the second most abundant mineral on Earth. Quartz crystals have piezo-electric characteristics which means that they produce an electrical potential when under mechanical stress. The resonant frequency of a quartz crystal is dependent on its shape and size and can be adjusted precisely by altering its mechanical loading. This frequency can be used to accurately provide a stable clock signal for radio oscillators and for timing signals in digital electronic circuits. They are manufactured for frequencies from a few tens of kiloHertz to tens of megaHertz and are found in wristwatches, clocks, radios and computers.

A quartz crystal cpmponent.

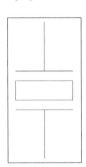

Electronic symbol for a quartz crystal.

A crystal behaves like an RLC (resistor, inductor, capacitor) circuit but has the advantage that its frequency is very stable and does not change significantly with temperature or ageing.

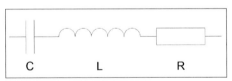

Equivalent RLC circuit.

A quartz crystal has a resonant frequency such that when a random noise AC signal is applied to two plates either side of the crystal a small portion of that noise will be at the resonant frequency of the crystal and the crystal will start oscillating at that frequency. The oscillator circuit will then amplify the resonant frequency to such an extent that it will dominate the output of the oscillator. The final output of the oscillator can either be the fundamental frequency of the crystal or one of its multiples or overtones. In high frequency oscillators this can be the third, fifth or seventh overtone.

A simple oscillator circuit can be implemented using an inverter gate and a quartz crystal to produce a very precise clock pulse for use in TTL circuits using the arrangement below.

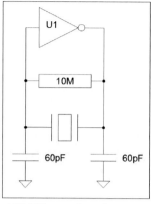

A CMOS crystal oscillator.

21 CELLS AND BATTERIES

A battery is a device that converts chemical energy directly to electrical energy. The first battery was invented by Alessandro Volta in 1800 and was called a Voltaic pile. Batteries are now a very common portable power source for all sorts of household and industrial appliances.

A battery is made up of a number of Voltaic cells; each Voltaic cell is made up of two half-cells. One of the half cells contains an electrolyte and an electrode (cathode) to which the positively charged ions are attracted and the other half cell contains an electrolyte and an electrode (anode) to which the negatively charged ions are attracted. An oxidation (redox) process takes place that adds electrons to the cathode and removes them from the anode and a potential difference (*pd*) is developed across the electrodes. When the cell is neither charging nor discharging the *pd* is called the open-circuit Voltage and is equal to the electromotive force (emf) of the cell. An ideal battery would have no internal resistance and the battery would maintain a constant emf until the battery is exhausted, however, in reality there is an internal resistance which increases as the battery discharges which causes the emf to decrease under discharge.

Various cells and batteries.

Symbol for a battery. It depicts a Voltaic pile.

Dry and wet cells

Dry cells are made from a variety of moist paste electrolytes, including alkaline and zinc carbon which both produce about 1.5 Volts per cell, NiCd and NiMH which produce about 1.2 Volts per cell and lithium cells that produce about 3 Volts per cell. A 9 Volt alkaline battery would therefore require six cells.

Wet cells are made using a liquid or gel electrolyte and are typically lead-acid or nickel-cadmium. They are often still used for cars and standby power for uninterruptible power supplies.

Primary and secondary cells

Primary batteries when discharged cannot be recharged and are therefore disposable; they are very common and are ready for use immediately after manufacture. Secondary batteries are rechargeable and can be used many times over; they are also fairly common but generally have to be charged before first use. Rechargeable batteries have their chemical reactions reversed by applying an external Voltage source to the electrodes; however there is a limit to the number of times a battery can be recharged as eventually there will be a loss of electrolyte and some electrode corrosion. The lead-acid battery is the oldest and most common form of rechargeable battery, however there are dry batteries such as lithium-ion that are rechargeable too.

Battery discharge time

Some batteries will have their capacity given as a product of current and time and will be labelled as Ah. For example, in theory, a 100Ah battery could supply its Voltage at 100 Amps for one hour, 50 Amps for two hours or 1 Amp for 100 hours. In practice there are a few other factors such as temperature that will affect capacity and in general a battery is more efficient at lower discharge currents than higher discharge rates.

22 AC THEORY

AC means *Alternating Current*, and this is different from DC which means *Direct Current*. Most electronics is performed with a DC Voltage, however an important part of electronics is how an AC circuit works. An AC Voltage alternates its current direction every so often. Mains electricity is AC and alternates its current direction at a sinusoidal frequency of 50Hz (in the UK) which is every 20mS. Radio signals and audio signals are also AC, usually at much higher frequencies and may have quite a complex waveform. The simplest waveform for an AC Voltage is a sine wave at a fixed frequency, this is because it is a single frequency without any harmonics. Other

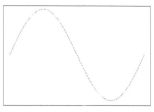

Sine wave.

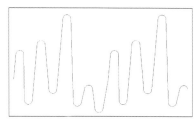

Complex wave.

waveforms such as a square wave, saw tooth, sound, light and video are also AC but are usually quite complex containing many different frequencies and harmonics. For the purpose of understanding AC theory we shall limit ourselves to a single sine wave rather than complex periodic waves.

Phase relationship R, L & C

In a purely resistive R circuit the Voltage and current change at the same time. Therefore as the Voltage of the sine wave passes through zero so does the current. They are in phase with each other (0°).

In an inductive L circuit, the Voltage and current are not in phase with each other. The inductance opposes change due to the back emf induced. This causes the current to reach its peak sometime after the Voltage peaks. Therefore in an inductive circuit, the current 'lags' the Voltage. In a purely inductive circuit the current will lag by a quarter of a cycle (-90°).

In a capacitive C circuit the Voltage and current are also not in phase with each other. Capacitance has the effect of delaying Voltage as the capacitor charges up. Therefore in a capacitive circuit the current 'leads' the Voltage. In a purely capacitive circuit the Voltage will peak a quarter of a cycle ($+90°$) after the current peaks. Therefore it is opposite to inductance.

Reactance

Inductive reactance X_L

As the current in an inductor changes a back emf is generated that opposes the change in current. The faster that the current changes, i.e. the higher the frequency, the larger the back emf produced which in turn reduces current flow. The opposition to current flow in an inductor is called inductive reactance (X_L) (measured in Ohms) and is dependent on both the frequency of the alternating current and the inductance of the inductor (measured in Henries).

$$X_L = 2\pi f L$$

Capacitive reactance X_C

As the current in a capacitor changes the capacitor charges up. If the frequency is high then the capacitor will not have time to fully charge before the current is reversed and has to start charging again. Current passes through a capacitor more easily when it is not in its zero current state therefore as the frequency of the AC waveform increases the current flow increases. This frequency dependent opposition to current flow is called capacitive reactance (X_C) and is also measured in ohms.

$$X_C = 1/2\pi f C$$

Impedance Z

Impedance (Z) is the combined effect of resistance R, inductive reactance X_L and capacitive reactance X_C in an AC circuit, whether in a single component or the circuit as a whole. Impedance is measured in Ohms (like resistance) and is a measurement of the overall opposition to AC current at a particular frequency. As explained earlier the inductance and hence inductive reactance lags the resistance component of impedance and the capacitance and hence the capacitive inductance leads the resistive component of impedance. Impedance is therefore a vector sum of the three components, resistance R, inductive reactance (X_L) and capacitive reactance (X_c). The resistive component is in phase, $0°$,

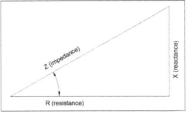

Impedance triangle.

and the reactive components are at opposite $90°$ to each other. Therefore the overall reactance is the difference between X_L and X_c, Impedance then becomes a simple Pythagoras triangle, where resistance and overall reactance are $90°$ to each other and Impedance is the hypotenuse.

$$Z = \sqrt{(R^2 + (X_L - X_c)^2)}$$

Filters

By combining resistors, inductors and capacitors in different ways in an AC circuit the current flow at different frequencies can be manipulated. A low pass filter can be used to remove or attenuate higher frequencies and let lower frequencies pass, for example to cut treble frequencies in a sub-woofer speaker.

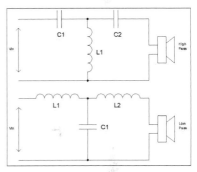

High pass and low pass filter.

A high pass filter can be used to remove lower frequencies and let higher frequencies pass, perhaps to a tweeter speaker.

A band pass filter is a combination of high pass and low pass filters in a T arrangement that allows a select range of frequencies to pass but attenuates higher and lower frequencies. A variation of this is the band stop filter which will pass frequencies above and below the designated stop band. These are commonly used in IF (intermediate frequency) stages in radio receivers.

Series RLC circuit

If a resistor, inductor and capacitor are wired in series and an AC Voltage applied to it, a current will flow. And because it is a series circuit, the current must be the same through all three components at any one time. As the frequency of the applied AC Voltage changes the resistance will remain the same but the reactances of the other

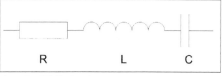

A series RLC circuit.

two components will change. The overall impedance will change with frequency but there will be a point where the capacitive reactance and the inductive reactance will cancel each other out and leave a purely resistive circuit. This magic spot is called the series resonance.

Parallel (R)LC circuit

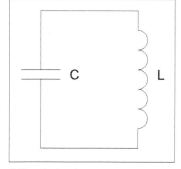

If an inductor and capacitor are wired in parallel and AC Voltage applied to it, a current will flow. At the resonant frequency the reactances of the inductor and capacitor will be equal such that equal but opposite currents will be flowing through each side of the circuit. In an ideal LC circuit the resultant supply current is zero, however there will be some resistance so some current

LC tank circuit.

will be drawn. However, to the AC supply Voltage this appears to have infinite impedance as current flows from C to L and back again. Current is therefore effectively stored within the parallel circuit at resonance without being released to the rest of the circuit. For this reason this is sometimes called a 'tank' circuit and is widely used for tuning circuits in radio and oscillators.

The resonant frequency of both the series and parallel RLC circuit is (ignoring R).

$$f^r = 1/(2\pi\sqrt{LC})$$

23 TRANSFORMERS

A transformer consists of two inductively coupled conductors, the transformers coils, that can transfer an alternating current (AC) in the first or *primary* winding into the *secondary* winding. This effect is called inductive coupling and is achieved by the fact that the varying current in the first winding creates a varying magnetic flux in the transformer's core and thus a varying magnetic field through the secondary winding. A load is then connected to the secondary winding such that current flows

A transformer.

and energy is transferred from the primary circuit through the transformer to the load.

Transformers are generally very efficient in that about 98% of the energy is transferred with very little loss and so for practical purposes are considered to be 100% efficient and therefore *ideal*. An ideal transformer will have a secondary Voltage (V_s) induced into the secondary winding that is proportional to the primary Voltage (V_p) in the primary winding and that proportion is the ratio of the number of turns in the Primary winding (N_p) to the secondary winding (N_s).

$$\frac{Vs}{Vp} = \frac{Ns}{Np}$$

Therefore by selecting the number of turns in the primary and secondary windings of a transformer it is possible to 'step up' or 'step down' an AC Voltage.

Transformers can range in size from the very small transformers inside microphones to huge devices weighing hundreds of tons for the national grid. The vast majority of transformers are used to step down mains Voltage to a non-lethal Voltage for electronic

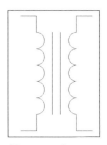

Diagram of a transformer.

equipment; they all, however, use the same basic principle outlined above.

Where the turns in the primary winding are equal to the turns in the secondary winding the secondary Voltage will be equal to the primary Voltage. This is known as an isolating transformer because there is no electrical connection between the primary and secondary Voltages, only a magnetic connection.

VA rating

The size of a transformer is determined by its VA rating. This is the Voltage multiplied by the Amperage (current), which, from Ohms Law, gives its power rating. The VA on the primary is equal to the VA on the secondary (less minimal losses) therefore if the transformer has, say, a N_p/N_s windings ratio of 20:1 and 240 Volts AC at the primary there will be 12 Volts AC at the secondary. If the VA rating for the transformer is 60VA then the maximum current available at the secondary is $60/12 = 5$ Amps. The maximum current that can be drawn at the primary is $60/240 = 0.25$ Amps (250mA). It is normal practice to size a transformer with a VA rating double at which is actually required. It can be seen therefore that as the secondary Voltage is stepped down the available current goes up whilst if the transformer steps up the Voltage then less current will be available at the secondary.

Audio transformers

Audio transformers are designed to be used in audio circuits. They can be used to block a DC component of an audio signal or to split or combine audio circuits or to provide impedance matching such as the high impedance output of a valve amplifier to the low impedance input of a speaker. Audio transformers can be used for very low level signals, such as those from a microphone to step up the low impedance output of a transformer to the high impedance input of a valve amplifier.

24 POWER SUPPLIES

Most electronic systems require a low Voltage DC (Direct Current) power supply, and the most readily available power supply is usually a medium Voltage AC (Alternating Current) supply. Some electronic control systems are battery powered, which is DC, but for most other control systems it is quite normal to convert the medium AC Voltage to a low DC Voltage. This is done using a power supply unit (PSU). There are two main types of PSU: linear and switching. A linear PSU converts the input power directly, usually with a transformer, bridge rectifier, smoothing capacitor and linear regulator. The linear regulator (when used) is not very efficient and converts lost Voltage to heat. A switching PSU (switch-mode), switches its input power on and off very quickly and spends most of its time off when converting to a much lower Voltage such that the output is a smoothed average Voltage.

Linear PSU

Most linear power supplies use the AC mains supply (240V AC, 50Hz in the UK) as the input Voltage which is then transformed down to a lower (occasionally higher) AC Voltage by a transformer. The transformed AC Voltage is then fed to a rectifier to produce a 'lumpy' DC Voltage. This lumpy Voltage is then usually smoothed out using an electrolytic capacitor. Some simple power supplies will output at the rectifier without smoothing or at the smoothing capacitor with smoothing. This would then be an unregulated power supply. However, most power supplies have a Voltage regulator to keep the output Voltage steady under varying load conditions and a current limiting function to protect the rest of the

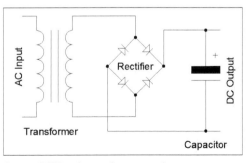

Linear PSU without a linear regulator.

power supply from damage in the event of excessive overcurrent. The Voltage regulator will also reduce any residual ripple and noise on the output Voltage.

The transformed AC Voltage will be at a ratio of the primary and secondary windings of the transformer. For example, if the primary to secondary winding ratio is 10:1 and the input Voltage is 240 Volts AC, the transformed Voltage will be 24 Volts AC. The output of the rectifier will depend on whether it is a half wave rectifier (one diode) or a full wave rectifier (two diodes) or full bridge rectifier (four diodes).

A half wave rectifier will rectify only one half of the incoming AC waveform with one diode so that the average (RMS, root mean square) output Voltage is 0.45 of the input AC Voltage.

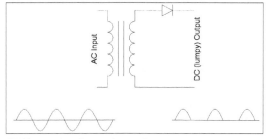

Half wave rectifier and waveform.

A full wave rectifier will rectify both halves of the incoming waveform with two diodes so that the average (RMS) output Voltage is 0.9 of the input AC Voltage. This circuit requires a centre-tapped transformer.

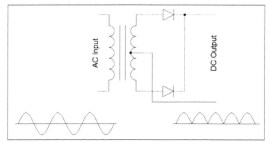

Centre tapped transformer full wave rectifier and waveform.

A full wave bridge rectifier will rectify both halves of the incoming waveform with four diodes so that the average (RMS) output Voltage is 0.9 of the input AC Voltage. This circuit does not require a centre-tapped transformer.

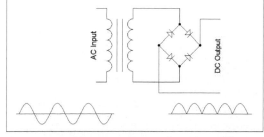

Transformer full wave bridge rectifier and waveform.

Smoothing capacitor

The output of any of the above rectifier circuits will produce a 'lumpy' DC Voltage; this Voltage can still be used by some simple items such as relays, contactors, lamps, DC motors and solenoids. However, most electronic circuits will require a much smoother DC Voltage. This is achieved by using an electrolytic capacitor as a tank circuit. An analogy of the electrolytic capacitor tank circuit is to imagine a tank of water being filled with spurts of water from above but producing a steady flow from a tap at the base. In a similar way the lumpy DC charges up the capacitor from peak to peak and if the capacitor is big enough the discharge will be relatively slow allowing a smooth output Voltage. The effect of this also raises the average output DC Voltage. In general an electrolytic capacitor of at least 100 µF is required and it must be rated for the maximum (peak) Voltage of the secondary AC Voltage.

Voltage regulator

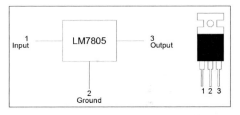

Most power supplies will require a fixed output Voltage: 5 Volts DC, 10 Volts DC, 12 Volts DC and 24 Volts DC are very common. Some power supplies, particularly a bench power supply will require a variable DC output. Whether fixed or variable, in order to achieve a steady output Voltage under varying load conditions and to protect the rest of the power supply a Voltage regulator is used. The simplest fixed Voltage regulator is the 78XX series. The xx denotes the output Voltage. For example a 7805 is a 5 Volt regulator, they are available in various current ratings with their construction as robust as required depending on which current rating is required. A common LM7805 is a 5 Volt 1 Amp device in a three pin TO220 form. There is an input pin, output pin and a common zero Volt pin. The input Voltage must be higher than the output Voltage by at least two or three Volts in order for the device to work. If the input Voltage is much higher

7805 Voltage regulator.

the Voltage regulator output Voltage then it will be dissipating a lot of heat and a heatsink will be required. There is also a 79xx series of Voltage regulators for negative Voltage applications.

Switched PSU

A switched mode power supply rectifies the incoming AC Voltage directly to produce a high DC Voltage. This DC Voltage is then switched on and off at a very high frequency, typically greater than 10kHz, to produce a very high frequency AC Voltage. This Voltage is then transformed down using a much smaller and lighter transformer than a linear PSU and is then rectified and smoothed. A switch mode power supply will

Switch-mode psu.

have a Voltage regulator and will often have advanced current limiting abilities to protect the sensitive switching electronics. They very often have a 'crowbar' circuit that 'folds back' the output Voltage if an external short circuit is detected to further protect itself. The switch mode power supply will also often have power factor correction components in its input circuit to prevent unwanted harmonics from the switching circuit affecting other electronic equipment using the same power supply.

25 LEDs

A Light Emitting Diode (LED) functions just like an ordinary diode except that it emits light when forward-biased; this phenomenon is called electroluminescence. They are normally made from gallium arsenide phosphide (GaAsP), gallium phosphide (GaP) or gallium arsenide (GaAs). They can emit red, green, yellow or blue light. They are very useful as indicators and when many LEDs are grouped together they

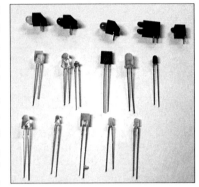

Various LEDs.

can create a significant light source. White LEDs are a combination of blue and Ultraviolet LEDs with yellow phosphor. They are extremely reliable, especially when compared to incandescent light bulbs, and can be switched very quickly making them suitable for displays and communications. A special form of the LED is the IRED which emits light in the infra red spectrum at about 50 times stronger than 'normal' visible LEDs. The IRED is particularly useful for remote controls and light-barriers.

The forward Voltage is from about 1.5 Volts to 3 Volts according to the type and it begins to emit light at about 1mA. A series resistor is normally used to limit the current to about 20mA. When current is flowing through the LED energy is released as photons.

Colour	Material	Forward Voltage	Wavelength
Infrared	Gallium Arsenide (GaAs)	1.2 to 1.4 V	>760nm
Red	Gallium Arsenide Phosphide (GaAsP)	1.4 to 1.8 V	$610 < \lambda < 760nm$
Orange	Gallium Arsenide Phosphide (GaAsP)	2.03 to 2.1 V	$590 < \lambda < 610nm$

Colour	Material	Forward Voltage	Wavelength
Yellow	Gallium Arsenide Phosphide (GaAsP)	2.0 to 2.6 V	570 < λ < 590nm
Green	Gallium Arsenide Phosphide (GaAsP)	2.2 to 2.8 V	500 < λ < 570nm
Blue	Zinc Selenide (ZnSe)	2.48 to 3.7 V	450 < λ < 500nm
Ultraviolet	Aluminium gallium nitride (AlGaN)	3.1 to 4.4 V	< 400nm
White	Blue/UV diode with yellow phosphor	3.5 V	Broad spectrum

To find the value of the series resistor, you should determine the Volt drop across the resistor and (using Ohm's Law) divide it by the current.

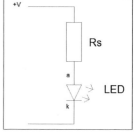

LED with series resistor.

For example, if you wanted to illuminate a green LED quite brightly from 24V DC, the calculation would be as follows:

Volt drop across the resistor = 24V – 2.2V = 21.8V

Value of required resistor = 21.8V/20mA = 1090Ω

The nearest preferred value would a 1KΩ resistor. A higher value resistor would produce a dimmer light and lower value resistor would produce a greater light (or damage the LED). Each LED should have its own series resistor.

26 LIGHT SENSORS

There are several types of electronic light sensors, these being:

Light dependent resistor (LDR)

Photodiode

Phototransistor

Light Dependent Resistor

Opto-couplers

The resistance of a Light Dependent Resistor (LDR) or photo-resistor decreases with increasing light intensity. They are cheap and easy to use. An LDR is made from a high resistance semiconductor material such as cadmium sulphide and when high frequency photons hit the material the semiconductors electrons become free which in turn lowers the resistance. They are primarily used for light meters, alarm clocks and outdoor clocks. Other semiconductor

Light dependent resistor.

materials such as lead sulphide or indium antimonide can be used for mid-range infrared sensor applications and germanium copper is used for the best far-infrared detectors and are used for infrared astronomy and infrared spectroscopy. LDRs have the advantage that they can be used with alternating current (AC) but their main disadvantage is that their response time is much slower than for other light sensors, typically around 200mS.

Photodiode

All semiconductor PN junctions are sensitive to light to some extent; that is when light falls on them electrons are freed allowing current to flow. This is known at the 'photoelectric effect'. This is normally an undesired side-effect so diodes, transistors and integrated circuits are packaged in encapsulated opaque material so as to reduce this effect. However, the photodiode exploits this phenomenon and uses the photocurrent to convert light into Voltage or current depending on its mode of operation.

When used in *photovoltaic mode*, the photocurrent flow out of the device is reduced and a small Voltage develops. This mode exploits the photovoltaic effect, which is the basis for solar cells; a solar cell will produce about 0.5 Volts in strong sunlight and they can be connected together in series to produce a small power source.

In photoconductive mode, the diode is reverse biased, which increases the width of the depletion layer, which will decrease the PN junction's capacitance resulting in a faster response time. The reverse bias will induce only a small amount of back current whilst the photocurrent is linearly proportional to the light falling on it. Although this mode is faster, it tends to exhibit more electronic noise

Phototransistor

A phototransistor again uses the 'photoelectric effect' and is normally constructed as an NPN transistor with the base connection missing. Light falling on the exposed base region causes the transistor to conduct from emitter to collector. Where a base connection is present it is only used to bias the transistor and can be used to adjust the transistor's response to light.

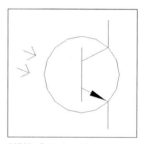

NPN phototransistor.

Opto-Coupler

An opto-coupler (or opto-isolator) is a device used to connect two parts of an electronic circuit by light thus electrically isolating them from each other. This is particularly useful if the two parts of the electronic circuit are using different Voltages. The input of an opto-coupler is typically a light emitting diode (LED) that produces a light source when it is forward-biased. This light will then fall on a phototransistor that will then conduct. Both components will be encapsulated in an opaque material such that only the light of the LED will affect

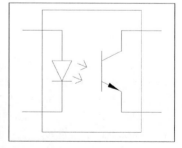

Opto-isolator.

the output phototransistor. There may be several LED/phototransistor pairs in a single device. The electrical insulation is typically proof against thousands of Volts. Other variations of the opto-coupler are using a photodiode in photoconductive mode at the output or for high power applications using a triac at the output.

27 THERMAL SENSORS

Thermal sensors are used to measure temperature. There are several types of thermal sensor, these being:
>Thermistor
>Band gap sensor
>Platinum Resistance element
>Thermocouple
>Temperature switch

Thermistor

The thermistor is basically a resistor that changes its resistance with temperature. There are two types of thermistor: the PTC and the NTC thermistor. The abbreviations PTC and NTC come from their descriptions 'positive temperature coefficient' and negative temperature coefficient' respectively.

A thermistor.

The resistance of a PTC thermistor increases with temperature and the resistance of an NTC thermistor decreases with temperature. The PTC thermistor is mainly used as a protective element in circuits to prevent over-temperature whereas the NTC thermistor is mainly used as a temperature sensor and for temperature compensation in semiconductor circuits.

PTC thermistors are mainly used for 'over-temperature' sensing. The 'over-temperature' type has a normal resistance of about 100Ω, but above a set temperature the resistance will very quickly reach 10KΩ. The PTC thermistor can be wired in series with loads of up to 350mA that is getting hot because of 'over-current'; the increase in resistance will reduce the current. Otherwise the PTC can be wired into a comparator (see Op-Amps) type circuit and then interfaced with circuitry to bring the temperature down to acceptable levels.

NTC thermsitors are available in several formats such as beads, bars and discs. The NTC thermistor can have resistance values from 25Ω

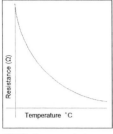

NTC characteristic.

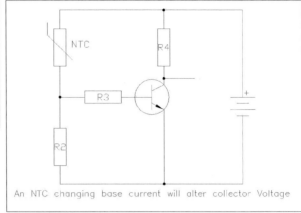

An NTC changing base current will alter collector Voltage

NTC controlling base current.

up to about 1MΩ with tolerances from 10% to 20%. An NTC thermistor would generally control the base current in a transistor such that the transistors collector current could control whatever it is that requires temperature measurement or control.

Band Gap Sensor

A band-gap sensor relies on the fact that the forward Voltage of a diode is temperature dependent. They can therefore be included in an integrated circuit very cheaply and used to monitor the temperature of itself. They are also available as a standalone temperature sensor and are very common in electronic circuits that require temperature monitoring. An example of this would be the LM35CZ which produces an output of 0V to 1.1V over the temperature range 0°C to 110°C.

Platinum Resistance Element

A resistance element thermometer is a device that changes its resistance with temperature. The most widely used one is the platinum resistance element because of its change of resistance is very linear and because it is chemically inert. They are widely used in industrial applications but are relatively expensive. They normally have a resistance of 100Ω at 0°C to 138.5Ω at 100°C and are useable up to about 600°C. Because of the relatively small percentage change they are often used in a 'wheatstone bridge' configuration.

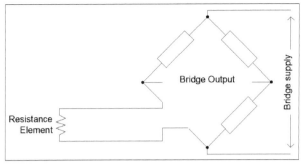

Wheatstone bridge with platinum resistance element.

Thermocouple

The thermocouple relies on the fact that a potential difference (*p.d.*) will develop across a junction of two dissimilar metals. The most common is the K type that uses the metals iron and constantan (a copper-nickel alloy) and will produce 41μV/°C. There are other types that use other metals that will produce higher Voltages per degree or have other useful properties such as being non-magnetic or higher temperature ranges. They are not as accurate as other forms of temperature sensing but they are very cheap and very predictable making them the most common form of temperature sensing.

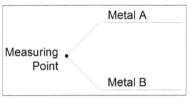

Diagram of a thermocouple.

Temperature switch

A temperature switch has a bi-metallic strip of two dissimilar metals such that when the temperature reaches a certain designated level the differing expansion rates of the two metals will cause the strip to bend so that can be used to either make or break an electrical circuit. They only provide an on/off signal and are not very accurate but they are very cheap. This type of sensor is widely used in water heating systems, domestic thermostats and simple over-temperature sensing devices.

28 RELAYS

A relay is an electrically operated switch, and most relays use an electromagnet to operate a switching mechanism. A relay is often used to allow a low power signal switch a high power circuit with complete electrical isolation or to switch multiple circuits with a single control signal. There are also solid-state relays that use semiconductors for the switching and thus have no moving parts.

Electromagnetic relay

An electromagnetic relay consists of a coil wrapped around a soft iron core called a yoke and

A typical electromagnetic relay.

a moveable iron armature that is physically connected to one or more sets of switching contacts. The armature is held in place by a spring such that when the coil is de-energised the armature is at rest but when the coil is energised the electromagnetic

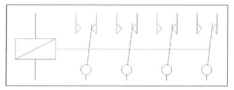

Circuit diagram of an electromagnetic relay with four sets of change-over contacts.

coil exerts a force on the armature against the spring and the contacts either 'make' or 'break' depending on the design.

The contacts are usually described as 'normally open', 'normally closed' or 'changeover'. A normally open contact is open circuit when the coil is de-energised, and closes when the coil is energised. A normally closed contact is closed circuit when the coil is de-energised and opens when the coil is energised. A changeover contact has a common contact and switches between the common and a normally closed contact when de-energised and the switches over to connect the common and normally open contact when energised.

The energising coil can either be a direct current (DC) coil or an alternating current (AC) coil. A DC coil will often have a diode connected across the coil to absorb the back-emf when the coil is de-energised (and the magnetic field collapses); this helps prevents spikes that may damage sensitive semiconductor components.

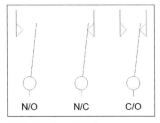

N/O, N/C and C/O contacts.

Latching relay

A latching relay is a special type of electromagnetic relay that, as its name suggests, holds the relay into one of its two states even when the coil current has been switched off. A latching relay may either have two coils, one to put it into each of the switched states (bistable) or it may have a single coil that requires a current of the opposite polarity in order to change its state. Latching relays are useful for simple memory circuits that 'remembers' its state even during a power outage or for circuits that can only provide a short duration pulse, perhaps to save power, but need to retain their state.

Contactor

A contactor is similar to a relay although not technically a relay and is used to switch heavy duty loads such as motors. Typical switching current ratings for contactors range from about 6 Amps up to several hundred Amps and they can have quite a loud clunking sound when they are energised or de-energised.

Solid state relay

A solid state relay (SSR) is an electronic component that provides the same function as an electromagnetic relay but without any moving parts. This makes them more reliable for long term use.

Force-guided relays

A relay that has it contacts mechanically linked together is known as a force-guided relay or positively guided relay. They are often used in safety circuits because if one set of contacts were to 'weld' or become immobilised another set of contacts could be used to monitor the fault in a safety circuit and ensure that a dangerous condition is avoided.

29 DIMMERS

Dimmers are electronic devices used to control the brightness of a lamp. By altering the AC Voltage waveform applied to a lamp the brightness can be controlled. Dimmers range in size from small domestic dimmers to high power units used in theatre and architectural lighting installations. Domestic dimmers tend to be controlled directly by a variable resistor and larger professional dimmers tend to be controlled by DMX or DALI often with an Ethernet protocol.

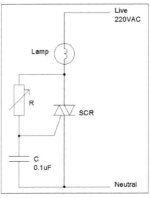

Triac based light dimmer.

Most dimmers are built using silicon controlled rectifiers (SCR) either a triac or a thyristor pair that control the firing angle to switch the lamp on and off such that the average amount of time that the SCR is conducting determines the brightness. Using this method an SCR will turn on at an adjustable time after the start of each alternating current half

Waveform of SCR switching at 90 degrees (50% brightness).

cycle and will switch off when the current cycle passes through zero Volts and will be ready to switch on again on the next half cycle.

A simple dimmer will use a capacitor and resistor charging circuit that will fire the SCR when the capacitor has charged to the trigger Voltage. The firing angle is adjusted by adjusting the value of the resistor in the RC timing circuit. A more advanced dimmer will use a microprocessor to trigger the SCR; this has the advantage of greater stability and the microprocessor can be programmed and controlled by digital electronics and software.

The SCR type dimmer produces some noise in the lamp itself and is also prone to emitting electromagnetic interference and as such will have quite a lot of circuitry just to suppress this noise.

Some newer dimmers use *insulated-gate bipolar transistors* (IGBT) and some even newer ones use sine-wave dimming which produces much less interference and noise.

30 FUSES AND BREAKERS

A fuse is an electrical device that ruptures or 'blows' when excessive current is drawn through it. When it ruptures it becomes open circuit thus isolating the electrical or electronic circuit that caused the overcurrent. The purpose is to prevent damage to the faulty electrical or electronic circuit downstream of the fuse and to

Various fuses and circuit breakers.

protect the upstream electrical supply and cables. It is a deliberate 'weak link' in the electrical supply chain and is designed to be sacrificial in the event of an overcurrent situation. An over current can occur because of a short circuit or because some part of the electronic circuit has failed in a way that causes excess current to flow or it may, for example, be a motor that has become mechanically stuck and is drawing too much current in its stalled state. Fuses are a 'lifed' item; that is they will fail eventually, so sometimes it ruptures for no apparent reason and if replaced the electronic circuit will continue to function without issue.

It is important that the correct rating (*In*) of fuse is used to protect a circuit. If the fuse rating is too low for the circuit it will rupture when there is no fault and if it is too high it may no longer be the weakest part of the supply chain and some other component or cable may rupture instead under fault conditions with the potential to start a fire.

Most electrical appliances in the UK are fitted with a 13 Amp plug, however this does not necessarily mean that it is correct to fit a 13 Amp fuse. For example, a table lamp with a 100 Watt light bulb will only draw (100W/240V) 0.42 Amps, so a 13 Amp fuse in its plug would be 30 times too great. A one or two amp fuse would be more suitable. In addition, if the flexible cable from the plug to the lamp had only 0.75mm sq. cable then the cable could fail before the fuse would blow.

Fuses come in all sorts of shapes and sizes, but apart from its physical dimensions there are three important parameters for any fuse, first its current rating as already mentioned and secondly its Voltage rating and thirdly its speed, i.e. how long will it stand an overload before rupturing. An inductive load such a motor with a heavy load to start will draw up to 12 or more times its running current during start up, so it needs a slow fuse, sometimes called an anti-surge fuse but an electronic circuit with semiconductors will need a fast fuse to prevent damage to them.

Fuse speeds can be summarised as follows:

Ultra rapid (FF)

Ten times rated current will rupture between 2mS and 4mS, used to protect very sensitive electronic equipment. These fuses are expensive but very fast. They are termed FF types or Super Quick Acting fuses.

Quick blow (F)

Ten times rated current will rupture between 5mS and 10mS. They are used to protect less sensitive equipment than the FF types and are therefore less expensive. They are termed F types or Quick Acting fuses.

Semi-delay

Ten times rated current will rupture between 15mS and 40mS. These fuses offer fairly rapid rupture performance under moderate current overloads, combined with some tolerance of moderate transient current surges. The fuse combines properties of the F type and T type fuses. They are termed Medium Time Lag or M type fuses.

Anti-surge

Ten times rated current will rupture between 40mS and 150mS, they are used to protect equipment from sustained overload currents but will allow high transient currents for a limited time. These fuses are expensive although provide a good means of protecting appliances that may have a high transient demand at switch-on (where FF types would blow) but low quiescent currents. They are termed Time Lag or T type fuses.

Circuit breakers

Circuit breakers perform the same task as fuses but are not sacrificial; they can be reset very quickly which is more convenient. They cost more than fuses but can be reset many times. They have to be selected to suit their intended load just like a fuse and have current, Voltage and a speed rating similar to that which a fuse has. However, a circuit breaker is generally much slower than a fuse and is not often seen on purely electronic equipment because of this.

ENTERTAINMENT TECHNOLOGY PRESS

FREE SUBSCRIPTION SERVICE

Keeping Up To Date with

Entertainment Electronics

Entertainment Technology titles are continually up-dated, and all major changes and additions are listed in date order in the relevant dedicated area of the publisher's website. Simply go to the front page of www.etnow.com and click on the BOOKS button. From there you can locate the title and be connected through to the latest information and services related to the publication.

The author of the title welcomes comments and suggestions about the book and can be contacted by email at: anton@avw.co.uk

Titles Published by Entertainment Technology Press

50 Rigging Calls *Chris Higgs, Cristiano Giavedoni 246pp* **£16.95**
ISBN: 9781904031758
Chris Higgs, author of ETP's two leading titles on rigging, An Introduction to Rigging in the Entertainment Industry and Rigging for Entertainment: Regulations and Practice, has collected together 50 articles he has provided regularly for Lighting + Sound International magazine from 2005 to date. They provide a wealth of information for those practising the craft within the entertainment technology industry. The book is profusely illustrated with caricature drawings by Christiano Giavedoni, featuring the popular rigging expert Mario.

ABC of Theatre Jargon *Francis Reid 106pp* **£9.95** ISBN: 9781904031093
This glossary of theatrical terminology explains the common words and phrases that are used in normal conversation between actors, directors, designers, technicians and managers.

Aluminium Structures in the Entertainment Industry *Peter Hind 234pp* **£24.95**
ISBN: 9781904031062
Aluminium Structures in the Entertainment Industry aims to educate the reader in all aspects of the design and safe usage of temporary and permanent aluminium structures specific to the entertainment industry – such as roof structures, PA towers, temporary staging, etc.

AutoCAD – A Handbook for Theatre Users *David Ripley 340pp* **£29.95**
ISBN: 9781904031741
From 'Setting Up' to 'Drawing in Three Dimensions' via 'Drawings Within Drawings', this compact and fully illustrated guide to AutoCAD covers everything from the basics to full colour rendering and remote 3D plotting. Third, completely revised edition, June 2014.

Automation in the Entertainment Industry – A User's Guide *Mark Ager and John Hastie 382pp* **£29.95** ISBN: 9781904031581
In the last 15 years, there has been a massive growth in the use of automation in entertainment, especially in theatres, and it is now recognised as its own discipline. However, it is still only used in around 5% of theatres worldwide. In the next 25 years, given current growth patterns, that figure will rise to 30%. This will mean that the majority of theatre personnel, including directors, designers, technical staff, actors and theatre management, will come into contact with automation for the first time at some point in their careers. This book is intended to provide insights and practical advice from those who use automation, to help the first-time user understand the issues and avoid the pitfalls in its implementation.

Basics – A Beginner's Guide to Lighting Design *Peter Coleman 92pp* **£9.95**
ISBN: 9781904031413
The fourth in the author's 'Basics' series, this title covers the subject area in four main sections: The Concept, Practical Matters, Related Issues and The Design Into Practice. In an

area that is difficult to be definitive, there are several things that cross all the boundaries of all lighting design and it's these areas that the author seeks to help with.

Basics – A Beginner's Guide to Special Effects *Peter Coleman 82pp* **£9.95**
ISBN: 9781904031338
This title introduces newcomers to the world of special effects. It describes all types of special effects including pyrotechnic, smoke and lighting effects, projections, noise machines, etc. It places emphasis on the safe storage, handling and use of pyrotechnics.

Basics – A Beginner's Guide to Stage Lighting *Peter Coleman 86pp* **£9.95**
ISBN: 9781904031208
This title does what it says: it introduces newcomers to the world of stage lighting. It will not teach the reader the art of lighting design, but will teach beginners much about the 'nuts and bolts' of stage lighting.

Basics – A Beginner's Guide to Stage Sound *Peter Coleman 86pp* **£9.95**
ISBN: 9781904031277
This title does what it says: it introduces newcomers to the world of stage sound. It will not teach the reader the art of sound design, but will teach beginners much about the background to sound reproduction in a theatrical environment.

Basics: A Beginner's Guide to Stage Management *Peter Coleman 64pp* **£7.95**
ISBN: 9781904031475
The fifth in Peter Coleman's popular 'Basics' series, this title provides a practical insight into, and the definition of, the role of stage management. Further chapters describe Cueing or 'Calling' the Show (the Prompt Book), and the Hardware and Training for Stage Management. This is a book about people and systems, without which most of the technical equipment used by others in the performance workplace couldn't function.

Building Better Theaters *Michael Mell 180pp* **£16.95** ISBN: 9781904031406
A title within our Consultancy Series, this book describes the process of designing a theatre, from the initial decision to build through to opening night. Michael Mell's book provides a step-by-step guide to the design and construction of performing arts facilities. Chapters discuss: assembling your team, selecting an architect, different construction methods, the architectural design process, construction of the theatre, theatrical systems and equipment, the stage, backstage, the auditorium, ADA requirements and the lobby. Each chapter clearly describes what to expect and how to avoid surprises. It is a must-read for architects, planners, performing arts groups, educators and anyone who may be considering building or renovating a theatre.

Carry on Fading *Francis Reid 216pp* **£20.00** ISBN: 9781904031642
This is a record of five of the best years of the author's life. Years so good that the only downside is the pangs of guilt at enjoying such contentment in a world full of misery induced by greed, envy and imposed ideologies. Fortunately Francis' DNA is high on luck, optimism and blessing counting.

Case Studies in Crowd Management
Chris Kemp, Iain Hill, Mick Upton, Mark Hamilton 206pp **£16.95**
ISBN: 9781904031482
This important work has been compiled from a series of research projects carried out by
the staff of the Centre for Crowd Management and Security Studies at Buckinghamshire
Chilterns University College (now Bucks New University), and seminar work carried out
in Berlin and Groningen with partner Yourope. It includes case studies, reports and a crowd
management safety plan for a major outdoor rock concert, safe management of rock concerts
utilising a triple barrier safety system and pan-European Health & Safety Issues.

Case Studies in Crowd Management, Security and Business Continuity
Chris Kemp, Patrick Smith 274pp **£24.95** ISBN: 9781904031635
The creation of good case studies to support work in progress and to give answers to those
seeking guidance in their quest to come to terms with perennial questions is no easy task.
The first Case Studies in Crowd Management book focused mainly on a series of festivals
and events that had a number of issues which required solving. This book focuses on a
series of events that had major issues that impacted on the every day delivery of the events
researched.

Close Protection – The Softer Skills *Geoffrey Padgham 132pp* **£11.95**
ISBN: 9781904031390
This is the first educational book in a new 'Security Series' for Entertainment
Technology Press, and it coincides with the launch of the new 'Protective Security
Management' Foundation Degree at Buckinghamshire Chilterns University College
(now Bucks New University). The author is a former full-career Metropolitan Police
Inspector from New Scotland Yard with 27 years' experience of close protection (CP).
For 22 of those years he specialised in operations and senior management duties with
the Royalty Protection Department at Buckingham Palace, followed by five years
in the private security industry specialising in CP training design and delivery. His
wealth of protection experience comes across throughout the text, which incorporates
sound advice and exceptional practical guidance, subtly separating fact from fiction.
This publication is an excellent form of reference material for experienced operatives,
students and trainees.

A Comparative Study of Crowd Behaviour at Two Major Music Events
Chris Kemp, Iain Hill, Mick Upton 78pp **£7.95** ISBN: 9781904031253
A compilation of the findings of reports made at two major live music concerts, and in
particular crowd behaviour, which is followed from ingress to egress.

Control Freak *Wayne Howell 270pp* **£28.95** ISBN: 9781904031550
Control Freak is the second book by Wayne Howell. It provides an in depth study of
DMX512 and the new RDM (Remote Device Management) standards. The book is aimed
at both users and developers and provides a wealth of real world information based on the
author's twenty year experience of lighting control.

Copenhagen Opera House *Richard Brett and John Offord* *272pp* **£32.00**
ISBN: 9781904031420
Completed in a little over three years, the Copenhagen Opera House opened with a royal gala performance on 15th January 2005. Built on a spacious brown-field site, the building is a landmark venue and this book provides the complete technical background story to an opera house set to become a benchmark for future design and planning. Sixteen chapters by relevant experts involved with the project cover everything from the planning of the auditorium and studio stage, the stage engineering, stage lighting and control and architectural lighting through to acoustic design and sound technology plus technical summaries.

Cue 80 *Francis Reid 310pp* **£17.95** ISBN: 9781904031659
Although Francis Reid's work in theatre has been visual rather than verbal, writing has provided crucial support. Putting words on paper has been the way in which he organised and clarified his thoughts. And in his self-confessed absence of drawing skills, writing has helped him find words to communicate his visual thinking in discussions with the rest of the creative team. As a by-product, this process of searching for the right words to help formulate and analyse ideas has resulted in half-a-century of articles in theatre journals.
Cue 80 is an anthology of these articles and is released in celebration of Francis' 80th birthday.

The DMX 512-A Handbook – Design and Implementation of DMX Enabled Products and Networks *James Eade 150pp* **£13.95** ISBN: 9781904031727
This guidebook was originally conceived as a guide to the new DMX512-A standard on behalf of the ESTA Controls Protocols Working Group (CPWG). It has subsequently been updated and is aimed at all levels of reader from technicians working with or servicing equipment in the field as well as manufacturers looking to build in DMX control to their lighting products. It also gives thorough guidance to consultants and designers looking to design DMX networks.

Electric Shadows: an Introduction to Video and Projection on Stage *Nick Moran 234pp* **£23.95** ISBN: 9781904031734
Electric Shadows aims to guide the emerging video designer through the many simple and difficult technical and aesthetic choices and decisions he or she has to make in taking their design from outline idea through to realisation. The main body of the book takes the reader through the process of deciding what content will be projected onto what screen or screens to make the best overall production design. The book will help you make electric shadows that capture the attention of your audience, to help you tell your stories in just the way you want.

Electrical Safety for Live Events *Marco van Beek 98pp* **£16.95** ISBN: 9781904031284
This title covers electrical safety regulations and good practise pertinent to the entertainment industries and includes some basic electrical theory as well as clarifying the "do's and don't's" of working with electricity.

Entertainment Electronics *Anton Woodward 154pp* **£15.95** ISBN: 9781904031819
Electronic engineering in theatres has become quite prevalent in recent years, whether for lighting, sound, automation or props – so it has become an increasingly important skill for

the theatre technician to possess. This book is intended to give the theatre technician a good grasp of the fundamental principles of electronics without getting too bogged down with maths so that many of the mysteries of electronics are revealed.

Entertainment in Production Volume 1: 1994-1999 *Rob Halliday 254pp* **£24.95**
ISBN: 9781904031512

Entertainment in Production Volume 2: 2000-2006 *Rob Halliday 242poo* £24.95
ISBN: 9781904031529
Rob Halliday has a dual career as a lighting designer/programmer and author and in these two volumes he provides the intriguing but comprehensive technical background stories behind the major musical productions and other notable projects spanning the period 1994 to 2005. Having been closely involved with the majority of the events described, the author is able to present a first-hand and all-encompassing portrayal of how many of the major shows across the past decade came into being. From *Oliver!* and *Miss Saigon* to *Mamma Mia!* and *Mary Poppins*, here the complete technical story unfolds. The books, which are profusely illustrated, are in large part an adapted selection of articles that first appeared in the magazine *Lighting&Sound International*.

Entertainment Technology Yearbook 2008 *John Offord 220pp* **£14.95**
ISBN: 9781904031543
The Entertainment Technology Yearbook 2008 covers the year 2007 and includes picture coverage of major industry exhibitions in Europe compiled from the pages of Entertainment Technology magazine and the etnow.com website, plus articles and pictures of production, equipment and project highlights of the year.

The Exeter Theatre Fire *David Anderson 202pp* **£24.95** ISBN: 9781904031130
This title is a fascinating insight into the events that led up to the disaster at the Theatre Royal, Exeter, on the night of September 5th 1887. The book details what went wrong, and the lessons that were learned from the event.

Fading into Retirement *Francis Reid 124pp* **£17.95**
ISBN: 9781904031352
This is the final book in Francis Reid's fading trilogy which, with Fading Light and Carry on Fading, updates the Hearing the Light record of places visited, performances seen, and people met. Never say never, but the author uses the 'final' label because decreasing mobility means that his ability to travel is diminished to the point that his life is now contained within a very few square miles. His memories are triggered by over 600 CDs, half of them Handel and 100 or so DVDs supplemented by a rental subscription to LOVEFiLM.

Fading Light – A Year in Retirement *Francis Reid 136pp* **£14.95**
ISBN: 9781904031352
Francis Reid, the lighting industry's favourite author, describes a full year in retirement. "Old age is much more fun than I expected," he says. Fading Light describes visits and experiences to the author's favourite theatres and opera houses, places of relaxation and re-visits to scholarly institutions.

Focus on Lighting Technology *Richard Cadena 120pp* **£17.95** ISBN: 9781904031147
This concise work unravels the mechanics behind modern performance lighting and appeals to designers and technicians alike. Packed with clear, easy-to-read diagrams, the book provides excellent explanations behind the technology of performance lighting.

The Followspot Guide *Nick Mobsby 450pp* **£28.95** ISBN: 9781904031499
The first in ETP's Equipment Series, Nick Mobsby's Followspot Guide tells you everything you need to know about followspots, from their history through to maintenance and usage. Its pages include a technical specification of 193 followspots from historical to the latest versions from major manufacturers.

From Ancient Rome to Rock 'n' Roll – a Review of the UK Leisure Security Industry
Mick Upton 198pp **£14.95** ISBN: 9781904031505
From stewarding, close protection and crowd management through to his engagement as a senior consultant Mick Upton has been ever present in the events industry. A founder of ShowSec International in 1982 he was its chairman until 2000. The author has led the way on training within the sector. He set up the ShowSec Training Centre and has acted as a consultant at the Bramshill Police College. He has been prominent in the development of courses at Buckinghamshire New University where he was awarded a Doctorate in 2005. Mick has received numerous industry awards. His book is a personal account of the development and professionalism of the sector across the past 50 years.

Gobos for Image Projection *Michael Hall and Julie Harper 176pp* **£25.95**
ISBN: 9781904031628
In this first published book dedicated totally to the gobo, the authors take the reader through from the history of projection to the development of the present day gobo. And there is broad practical advice and ample reference information to back it up. A feature of the work is the inclusion, interspersed throughout the text, of comment and personal experience in the use and application of gobos from over 25 leading lighting designers worldwide.

Health and Safety Aspects in the Live Music Industry *Chris Kemp, Iain Hill 300pp*
£30.00 ISBN: 9781904031222
This major work includes chapters on various safety aspects of live event production and is written by specialists in their particular areas of expertise.

Health and Safety in the Live Music and Event Technical Produciton Industry
Chris Hannam 74pp **£12.95** ISBN: 9781904031802
This book covers the real basics of health and safety in the live music and event production industry in a simple jargon free manner that can also be used as the perfect student course note accompaniment to the various safety passport schemes that now exist in our industry.

Health and Safety Management in the Live Music and Events Industry *Chris Hannam*
480pp **£25.95** ISBN: 9781904031307
This title covers the health and safety regulations and their application regarding all aspects

of staging live entertainment events, and is an invaluable manual for production managers and event organisers.

Hearing the Light – 50 Years Backstage *Francis Reid 280pp* **£24.95**
ISBN: 9781904031185
This highly enjoyable memoir delves deeply into the theatricality of the industry. The author's almost fanatical interest in opera, his formative period as lighting designer at Glyndebourne and his experiences as a theatre administrator, writer and teacher make for a broad and unique background.

Introduction to Live Sound *Roland Higham 174pp* **£16.95**
ISBN: 9781904031796
This new title aims to provide working engineers and newcomers alike with a concise knowledge base that explains some of the theory and principles that they will encounter every day. It should provide for the student and newcomer to the field a valuable compendium of helpful knowledge.

An Introduction to Rigging in the Entertainment Industry *Chris Higgs 272pp* **£24.95**
ISBN: 9781904031123
This title is a practical guide to rigging techniques and practices and also thoroughly covers safety issues and discusses the implications of working within recommended guidelines and regulations. Second edition revised September 2008.

Let There be Light – Entertainment Lighting Software Pioneers in Conversation
Robert Bell 390pp **£32.00** ISBN: 9781904031246
Robert Bell interviews a distinguished group of software engineers working on entertainment lighting ideas and products.

Light and Colour Filters *Michael Hall and Eddie Ruffell 286pp* **£23.95**
ISBN: 9781904031598
Written by two acknowledged and respected experts in the field, this book is destined to become the standard reference work on the subject. The title chronicles the development and use of colour filters and also describes how colour is perceived and how filters function. Up-to-date reference tables will help the practitioner make better and more specific choices of colour.

Lighting for Roméo and Juliette *John Offord 172pp* **£26.95** ISBN: 9781904031161
John Offord describes the making of the Vienna State Opera production from the lighting designer's viewpoint – from the point where director Jürgen Flimm made his decision not to use scenery or sets and simply employ the expertise of lighting designer Patrick Woodroffe.

Lighting Systems for TV Studios *Nick Mobsby 570pp* **£45.00** ISBN: 9781904031000
Lighting Systems for TV Studios, now in its second edition, is the first book specifically written on the subject and has become the 'standard' resource work for studio planning and design covering the key elements of system design, luminaires, dimming, control,

data networks and suspension systems as well as detailing the infrastructure items such as cyclorama, electrical and ventilation. TV lighting principles are explained and some history on TV broadcasting, camera technology and the equipment is provided to help set the scene! The second edition includes applications for sine wave and distributed dimming, moving lights, Ethernet and new cool lamp technology.

Lighting Techniques for Theatre-in-the-Round *Jackie Staines 188pp* **£24.95**
ISBN: 9781904031017
Lighting Techniques for Theatre-in-the-Round is a unique reference source for those working on lighting design for theatre-in-the-round for the first time. It is the first title to be published specifically on the subject and it also provides some anecdotes and ideas for more challenging shows, and attempts to blow away some of the myths surrounding lighting in this format.

Lighting the Diamond Jubilee Concert *Durham Marenghi 102pp* **£19.95**
ISBN: 9781904031673
In this highly personal landmark document the show's lighting designer Durham Marenghi pays tribute to the team of industry experts who each played an important role in bringing the Diamond Jubilee Concert to fruition, both for television and live audiences. The book contains colour production photography throughout and describes the production processes and the thinking behind them. In his Foreword, BBC Executive Producer Guy Freeman states: "Working with the whole lighting team on such a special project was a real treat for me and a fantastic achievement for them, which the pages of this book give a remarkable insight into."

Lighting the Stage *Francis Reid 120pp* **£14.95**   ISBN: 9781904031086
Lighting the Stage discusses the human relationships involved in lighting design – both between people, and between these people and technology. The book is written from a highly personal viewpoint and its 'thinking aloud' approach is one that Francis Reid has used in his writings over the past 30 years.

Miscellany of Lighting and Stagecraft *Michael Hall & Julie Harper 222pp* **£22.95**
ISBN: 9781904031680
This title will help schools, colleges, amateurs, technicians and all those interested in practical theatre and performance to understand, in an entertaining and informative way, the key backstage skills. Within its pages, numerous professionals share their own special knowledge and expertise, interspersed with diversions of historic interest and anecdotes from those practising at the front line of the industry. As a result, much of the advice and skills set out have not previously been set in print. The editors' intention with this book is to provide a Miscellany that is not ordered or categorised in strict fashion, but rather encourages the reader to flick through or dip into it, finding nuggets of information and anecdotes to entertain, inspire and engender curiosity – also to invite further research or exploration and generally encourage people to enter the industry and find out for themselves.

Mr Phipps' Theatre *Mark Jones, John Pick 172pp* £17.95 ISBN: 9781904031383
Mark Jones and John Pick describe "The Sensational Story of Eastbourne's Royal Hippodrome" – formerly Eastbourne Theatre Royal. An intriguing narrative, the book sets the story against a unique social history of the town. Peter Longman, former director of The Theatres Trust, provides the Foreword.

Northen Lights *Michael Northen 256pp* **£17.95** ISBN: 9781904031666
Many books have been written by famous personalities in the theatre about their lives and work. However this is probably one of the first memoirs by someone who has spent his entire career behind scenes, and not in front of the footlights. As a lighting designer and as consultant to designers and directors, Michael Northen worked through an exciting period of fifty years of theatrical history from the late nineteen thirties in theatres in the UK and abroad, and on productions ranging from Shakespeare, opera and ballet to straight plays, pantomimes and cabaret. This is not a complicated technical text book, but is intended to give an insight into some of the 300 productions in which he had been involved and some of the directors, the designers and backstage staff he have worked with, viewed from a new angle.

Pages From Stages *Anthony Field 204pp* **£17.95** ISBN: 9781904031260
Anthony Field explores the changing style of theatres including interior design, exterior design, ticket and seat prices, and levels of service, while questioning whether the theatre still exists as a place of entertainment for regular theatre-goers.

People, Places, Performances *Remembered by Francis Reid 60pp* **£8.95**
ISBN: 9781904031765
In growing older, the Author has found that memories, rather than featuring the events, increasingly tend to focus on the people who caused them, the places where they happened and the performances that arose. So Francis Reid has used these categories in endeavouring to compile a brief history of the second half of the twentieth century.

Performing Arts Technical Training Handbook 2013/2014 *ed: John Offord 304pp*
£19.95 ISBN: 9781904031710
Published in association with the ABTT (Association of British Theatre Technicians), this important Handbook, now in its third edition, includes fully detailed and indexed entries describing courses on backstage crafts offered by over 100 universities and colleges across the UK. A completely new research project, with accompanying website, the title also includes articles with advice for those considering a career 'behind the scenes', together with contact information and descriptions of the major organisations involved with industry training – plus details of companies offering training within their own premises.

Practical Dimming *Nick Mobsby 364pp* **£22.95** ISBN: 97819040313444
This important and easy to read title covers the history of electrical and electronic dimming, how dimmers work, current dimmer types from around the world, planning of a dimming system, looking at new sine wave dimming technology and distributed dimming. Integration of dimming into different performance venues as well as the necessary supporting electrical

systems are fully detailed. Significant levels of information are provided on the many different forms and costs of potential solutions as well as how to plan specific solutions. Architectural dimming for the likes of hotels, museums and shopping centres is included. Practical Dimming is a companion book to Practical DMX and is designed for all involved in the use, operation and design of dimming systems.

Practical DMX   *Nick Mobsby   276pp*   **£16.95**   ISBN: 9781904031369
In this highly topical and important title the author details the principles of DMX, how to plan a network, how to choose equipment and cables, with data on products from around the world, and how to install DMX networks for shows and on a permanently installed basis. The easy style of the book and the helpful fault finding tips, together with a review of different DMX testing devices provide an ideal companion for all lighting technicians and system designers. An introduction to Ethernet and Canbus networks are provided as well as tips on analogue networks and protocol conversion. It also includes a chapter on Remote Device Management.

A Practical Guide to Health and Safety in the Entertainment Industry
Marco van Beek   120pp   **£14.95**   ISBN: 9781904031048
This book is designed to provide a practical approach to Health and Safety within the Live Entertainment and Event industry. It gives industry-pertinent examples, and seeks to break down the myths surrounding Health and Safety.

Production Management   *Joe Aveline   134pp*   **£17.95**   ISBN: 9781904031109
Joe Aveline's book is an in-depth guide to the role of the Production Manager, and includes real-life practical examples and 'Aveline's Fables' – anecdotes of his experiences with real messages behind them.

Rigging for Entertainment: Regulations and Practice   *Chris Higgs   156pp*   **£19.95**
ISBN: 9781904031215
Continuing where he left off with his highly successful An Introduction to Rigging in the Entertainment Industry, Chris Higgs' second title covers the regulations and use of equipment in greater detail.

Rock Solid Ethernet   *Wayne Howell   304pp*   **£23.95**   ISBN: 9781904031697
Now in its third completely revised and reset edition, Rock Solid Ethernet is aimed specifically at specifiers, installers and users of entertainment industry systems, and will give the reader a thorough grounding in all aspects of computer networks, whatever industry they may work in. The inclusion of historical and technical 'sidebars' make for an enjoyable as well as an informative read.

Sixty Years of Light Work   *Fred Bentham   450pp*   **£26.95**   ISBN: 9781904031079
This title is an autobiography of one of the great names behind the development of modern stage lighting equipment and techniques. It includes a complete facsimile of the famous Strand Electric Catalogue of May 1936 – a reference work in itself.

Sound for the Stage *Patrick Finelli 218pp* **£24.95** ISBN: 9781904031154
Patrick Finelli's thorough manual covering all aspects of live and recorded sound for performance is a complete training course for anyone interested in working in the field of stage sound, and is a must for any student of sound.

Stage Automation *Anton Woodward 128pp* **£12.95** ISBN: 9781904031567
The purpose of this book is to explain the stage automation techniques used in modern theatre to achieve some of the spectacular visual effects seen in recent years. The book is targeted at automation operators, production managers, theatre technicians, stage engineering machinery manufacturers and theatre engineering students. Topics are covered in sufficient detail to provide an insight into the thought processes that the stage automation engineer has to consider when designing a control system to control stage machinery in a modern theatre. The author has worked on many stage automation projects and developed the award-winning Impressario stage automation system.

Stage Lighting Design in Britain: The Emergence of the Lighting Designer, 1881-1950
Nigel Morgan 300pp **£17.95** ISBN: 9781904031345
This title sets out to ascertain the main course of events and the controlling factors that determined the emergence of the theatre lighting designer in Britain, starting with the introduction of incandescent electric light to the stage, and ending at the time of the first public lighting design credits around 1950. The book explores the practitioners, equipment, installations and techniques of lighting design.

Stage Lighting for Theatre Designers *Nigel Morgan 124pp* **£17.95**
ISBN: 9781904031192
This is an updated second edition of Nigel Morgan's popular book for students of theatre design – outlining all the techniques of stage lighting design.

Technical Marketing Techniques *David Brooks, Andy Collier, Steve Norman 160pp*
£24.95 ISBN: 9781904031031
Technical Marketing is a novel concept, defined and elaborated by the authors of this book, with business-to-business companies competing in fast developing technical product sectors.

Technical Standards for Places of Entertainment *ABTT 354pp A4* **£45.00**
ISBN: 9781904031703
Technical Standards for Places of Entertainment details the necessary physical standards required for entertainment venues. Known in the industry as the "Yellow Book" the latest completely revised edition was first published in June 2013.

Theatre Engineering and Stage Machinery *Toshiro Ogawa 332pp* **£30.00**
ISBN: 9781904031024
Theatre Engineering and Stage Machinery is a unique reference work covering every aspect of theatrical machinery and stage technology in global terms, and across the complete historical spectrum. Revised February 2007.

Theatre Lighting in the Age of Gas *Terence Rees 232pp* **£24.95**
ISBN: 9781904031178
Entertainment Technology Press has republished this valuable historic work previously produced by the Society for Theatre Research in 1978. Theatre Lighting in the Age of Gas investigates the technological and artistic achievements of theatre lighting engineers from the 1700s to the late Victorian period.

Theatre Space: A Rediscovery Reported *Francis Reid 238pp* **£19.95**
ISBN: 9781904031437
In the post-war world of the 1950s and 60s, the format of theatre space became a matter for a debate that aroused passions of an intensity unknown before or since. The proscenium arch was clearly identified as the enemy, accused of forming a barrier to disrupt the relations between the actor and audience. An uneasy fellow-traveller at the time, Francis Reid later recorded his impressions whilst enjoying performances or working in theatres old and new and this book is an important collection of his writings in various theatrical journals from 1969-2001 including his contribution to the Cambridge Guide to the Theatre in 1988. It reports some of the flavour of the period when theatre architecture was rediscovering its past in a search to establish its future.

The Theatres and Concert Halls of Fellner and Helmer *Michael Sell 246pp* **£23.95**
ISBN: 9781904031772
This is the first British study of the works of the prolific Fellner and Helmer Atelier which was active from 1871-1914 during which time they produced over 80 theatre designs and are second in quantity only to Frank Matcham, to whom reference is made.
This period is one of great change as a number of serious theatre fires which included Nice and Vienna had the effect of the introduction of safety legislation which affected theatre design. This study seeks to show how Fellner and Helmer and Frank Matcham dealt with this increasing safety legislation, in particular the way in which safety was built into their new three part theatres equipped with iron stages, safety curtains, electricity and appropriate access and egress and, in the Vienna practice, how this was achieved across 13 countries.

Theatres of Achievement *John Higgins 302pp* **£29.95** ISBN: 9781904031376
John Higgins affectionately describes the history of 40 distinguished UK theatres in a personal tribute, each uniquely illustrated by the author. Completing each profile is colour photography by Adrian Eggleston.

Theatric Tourist *Francis Reid 220pp* **£19.95** ISBN: 9781904031468
Theatric Tourist is the delightful story of Francis Reid's visits across more than 50 years to theatres, theatre museums, performances and even movie theme parks. In his inimitable style, the author involves the reader within a personal experience of venues from the Legacy of Rome to theatres of the Renaissance and Eighteenth Century Baroque and the Gustavian Theatres of Stockholm. His performance experiences include Wagner in Beyreuth, the Pleasures of Tivoli and Wayang in Singapore. This is a 'must have' title for those who are as "incurably stagestruck" as the author.

Through the Viewfinder *Jeremy Hoare 276pp* **£21.95** ISBN:: 9781904031574
Do you want to be a top television cameraman? Well this is going to help!
Through the Viewfinder is aimed at media students wanting to be top professional television cameramen – but it will also be of interest to anyone who wants to know what goes on behind the cameras that bring so much into our homes.
The author takes his own opinionated look at how to operate a television camera based on 23 years' experience looking through many viewfinders for a major ITV network company. Based on interviews with people he has worked with, all leaders in the profession, the book is based on their views and opinions and is a highly revealing portrait of what happens behind the scenes in television production from a cameraman's point of view.

Walt Disney Concert Hall – The Backstage Story *Patricia MacKay & Richard Pilbrow 250pp* **£28.95** ISBN: 9781904031239
Spanning the 16-year history of the design and construction of the Walt Disney Concert Hall, this book provides a fresh and detailed behind the scenes story of the design and technology from a variety of viewpoints. This is the first book to reveal the "process" of the design of a concert hall.

Yesterday's Lights – A Revolution Reported *Francis Reid 352pp* **£26.95**
ISBN: 9781904031321
Set to help new generations to be aware of where the art and science of theatre lighting is coming from – and stimulate a nostalgia trip for those who lived through the period, Francis Reid's latest book has over 350 pages dedicated to the task, covering the 'revolution' from the fifties through to the present day. Although this is a highly personal account of the development of lighting design and technology and he admits that there are 'gaps', you'd be hard put to find anything of significance missing.

Go to www.etbooks.co.uk for full details of above titles and secure online ordering facilities. Most books also available for Kindle.